500 Dinosaur Puzzles and Quizzes

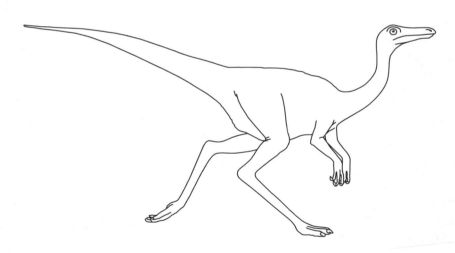

Bath · New York · Singapore · Hong Kong · Cologne · Delhi · Melbourne

D1473189

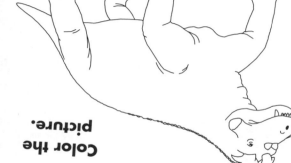

Color It

Color the picture.

4.

How many things can you think of beginning with the letter d? Draw a picture of them.

3. Dinosaur I-Spy

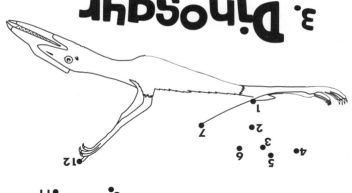

2. How Many?

How many eggs can you see in the picture? Circle them when you find them.

1. Flying Dot-to-Dot

Connect the dots to discover the flying reptile.

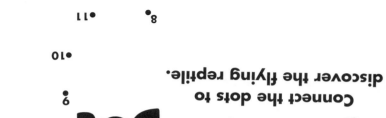

5. Roar!

Pretend to be your favorite dinosaur, **roaring**, and moving around exactly like the beast.

6. Odd One Out

Which dinosaur is different from the others?

7. Coloring Key

Use the key to color in the dinosaur picture.

a = green
b = yellow
c = red

8. Making Twins

Draw the missing parts to make the 2 dinosaurs the same.

3

9. Make a Copy

Copy the dinosaur into the grid and color it.

10. Footprints

Can you find all the dinosaur footprints hidden around these two pages? Ring them when you find them.

11. Find Things

Can you find these things around the page?

12. Color it

Color the picture.

Dragonfly   Leaves   Dinosaur

4

13. Counting Beasts

How many beasts can you count? Write the number in the box.

15. Describe

How would you describe this dinosaur?

14. Sorting Beasts

Prehistoric beasts come in all shapes and sizes. Can you put these beasts in size order? Write the number in the box beside them.

a.☐

b.☐

16. Colorful Beasts

Color each of these prehistoric beasts a different color, then write the color below it.

c.☐

_____

5

17. Find the Pairs

Draw a line between the pairs that are the same.

18. Favorite Dinosaur

Color all the dinosaurs. Then draw your favorite one in the box.

19. Different Diets

Some dinosaurs eat meat. Some dinosaurs eat plants. Put an M beside the dinosaur that eats meat. Put a P beside the dinosaur that eats plants.

20. Coloring

Color the meat-eating dinosaur red. Color the plant-eating dinosaur green.

21. Shadows

Connect each shadow to the correct prehistoric beast with a line.

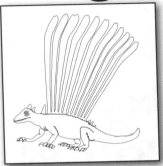

23. Odd One Out

Look at the beast in each box. Put an X through the one that is different.

22. Dinosaur Greeting Card

Make a card by folding a sheet of paper in half. Then copy the outline of a dinosaur shadow onto the front of the card. Decorate the dinosaur with a design.

7

24. Counting Fun

Can you count how many dinosaurs there are in each box? Write the number in the circle.

25. Dino Math

Solve each dinosaur problem and write the sum in the box.

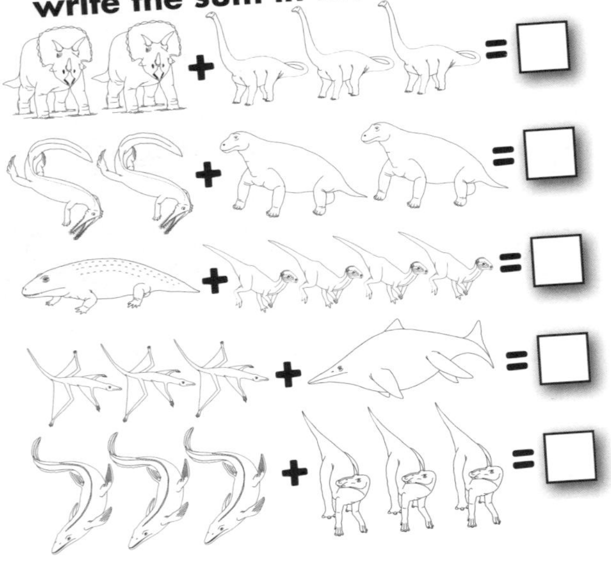

(2 triceratops) + (3 sauropods) = ☐

(2 dinosaurs) + (2 dinosaurs) = ☐

(1 dinosaur) + (3 dinosaurs) = ☐

(3 pterosaurs) + (1 ichthyosaur) = ☐

(3 plesiosaurs) + (2 pterosaurs) = ☐

26. Drawing Fun

Draw a dinosaur scene here. Then write a sentence about your picture on the line below.

27. Alphabet Picture

Connect the letters in the correct order to finish each picture.

g h i j k
f
e
l

d
c m n o
b p
a q

r

s
w t
x u
z v
y u

28. Coloring Fun

Color the biggest dinosaur yellow. Color the smallest dinosaur green.

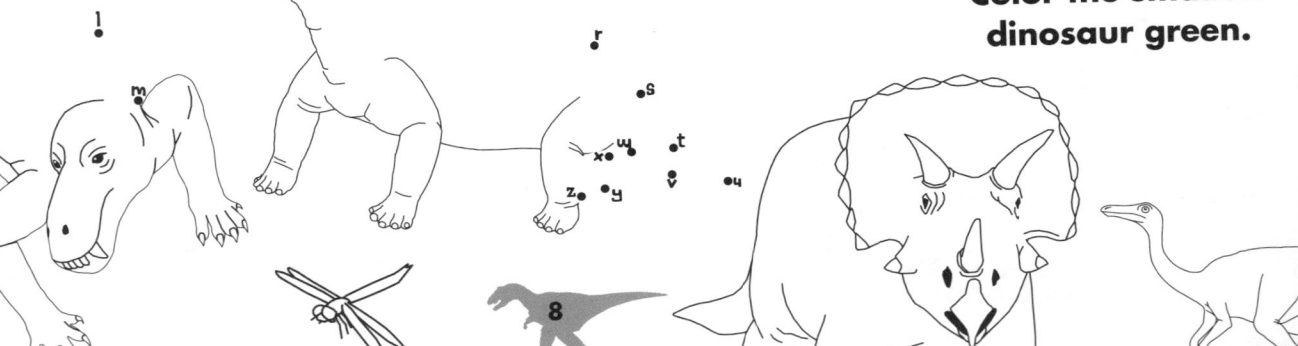

8

29. Word Ladder

The dinosaur walked up the hill to dig a hole. Change hill to hole in 3 moves by changing one letter at a time.

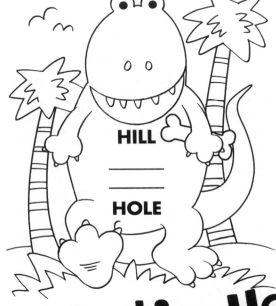

HILL
___
___
HOLE

30. What's He Got?

Why do you think the dinosaur wants to dig a hole? Can you see what he is carrying? Draw a picture of what he is carrying here.

31. Mixed-up Beasts

How many prehistoric beasts can you see in this picture? Write the number in the box.

32. Coloring

Color 4 of the beasts above.

9

33. Greedy Dino

This dinosaur is very hungry—how many bones has he hidden?

35. First Letter

Triceratops begins with the letter T. Brachiosaurus begins with the letter B. What letters do the other things on the page begin with?

36. Quick draw

Draw something else that begins with the letters **t** and **b**.

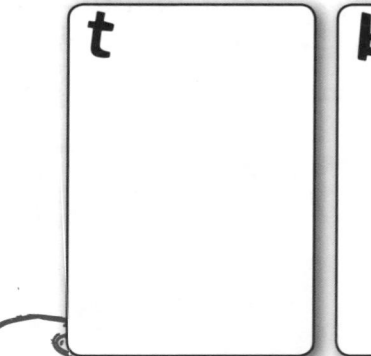

t	**b**

34. Color the bones you found

37. Hunt

How might a dino hunt its prey? Pretend to be hunting your prey and act it out for your friends.

38. Naming Dinosaurs

Can you think of any dinosaurs beginning with the letter T? Can you think of any dinosaurs beginning with the letter D?

39. Which Nest?

The mother dinosaur can't figure out which is her nest. Can you help her by using these clues?

It isn't the biggest nest.
It isn't the smallest nest.
It has **6** eggs in it.

40. Find the Babies

How many baby dinosaurs can you count on this page? Then, color the pictures.

Answer: 40. 4

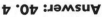

41. Silly Scene

Can you find 5 silly mistakes in this picture?

42. Coloring fun

Color the picture.

43. Dinosaur Maze

Help this dinosaur get through the jungle to find her baby.

44. Story Time

Why do you think the dinosaur lost her baby? Make up a story about what happened.

12

45. Storyboard

Put the pictures in the correct order.

[ ]   [ ]   [ ]

47. Copy

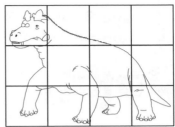

Copy this dinosaur into the grid below.

46. What Next?

What do you think might happen next? Draw a picture here.

48. Name Game

What name do you think would be good for this dinosaur? Decide what you want to call her, then write the name on the line below.

13

49. Who Is Hiding?

Shade in each section with a dot to discover a hidden picture.

51. Scrambled letters

Unscramble the letters to spell out what the dinosaur is carrying.

e	t	e	r

50. What might he be hiding from?

52. Color it

Color the picture above using this key.

1 = blue
2 = brown
3 = green
4 = yellow
5 = red

53. Dino teeth

These are dinosaur teeth and a skull like the ones you might see in a museum. How many teeth are there? Describe the teeth.

54.
What do you think the prehistoric creature whose skull this is would have looked like?

55. Snap your teeth like a **big** hungry dinosaur!

56. Different Reptiles

Color the reptile with a long neck **green**. Color the dinosaur with a long tail **red**.

15

57. Stepping-stones

The dinosaur can only step on stones that spell out the name of something you use to cross a river. Color the letters as you go. We have found the first letter for you.

58. Hidden Words

Can you find these words in the stepping-stones?

egg, dog, cat, bee

59. Missing

Find the correct pieces needed to complete the picture.

60. Finish It

Draw the missing pieces. Then color the picture.

61. Spot the Difference

Can you find **6** differences between these **2** pictures?

62. Coloring fun

Color both the pictures. Can you make them look as different as possible?

63. Naming

What can you see in each picture? Name all the things.

64. Dinosaur Picture

Draw a picture of a dinosaur and write the first letter of its name in the box.

Answer: 61. leaf in mouth, sun, back leg, extra spot on back, extra leaf on tree

65. Dotty Dinosaur

Join the dots to see what the dinosaur is eating.

66. Coloring Fun

Color the picture. Then write some words in the speech bubble.

67. Silly Dinosaur

Which things don't belong on this dinosaur?

68. Dinosaur Fun

Draw a picture of your own silly dinosaur.

Answer: 67. skateboard, banana, feather, silly nose.

69. Missing Letters

Fill in the missing letters in these words.

F _ SS _ L
BO _ E
_ ORN
_ _ IL
T _ _ TH

70. All Shapes and Sizes

Which is the tallest?
Which is the shortest?
Which is the fattest?
Which is the thinnest?

71. Finding Words

Can you find at least 8 words of 3 letters or more in the word PLATEOSAURUS? Write them in the Plateosaurus.

72. Drawing Fun

Draw your own picture of a Plateosaurus here. Then color it.

19

73. Color Fun

Decorate the dinosaur.

74. Parts of the Body

Which is the head? Which are the legs? Which is the tail? Write the names at the side.

75. Complete the Dino

Finish this dinosaur so that it looks the same as the other one.

76. Dinosaur Puzzle

Fill in the missing letters in these words.

T _ _ ANN _ SAUR _ _ R _ _ _
D _ PL _ _ OCUS
CL _ W
SW _ MP
J _ NGL _

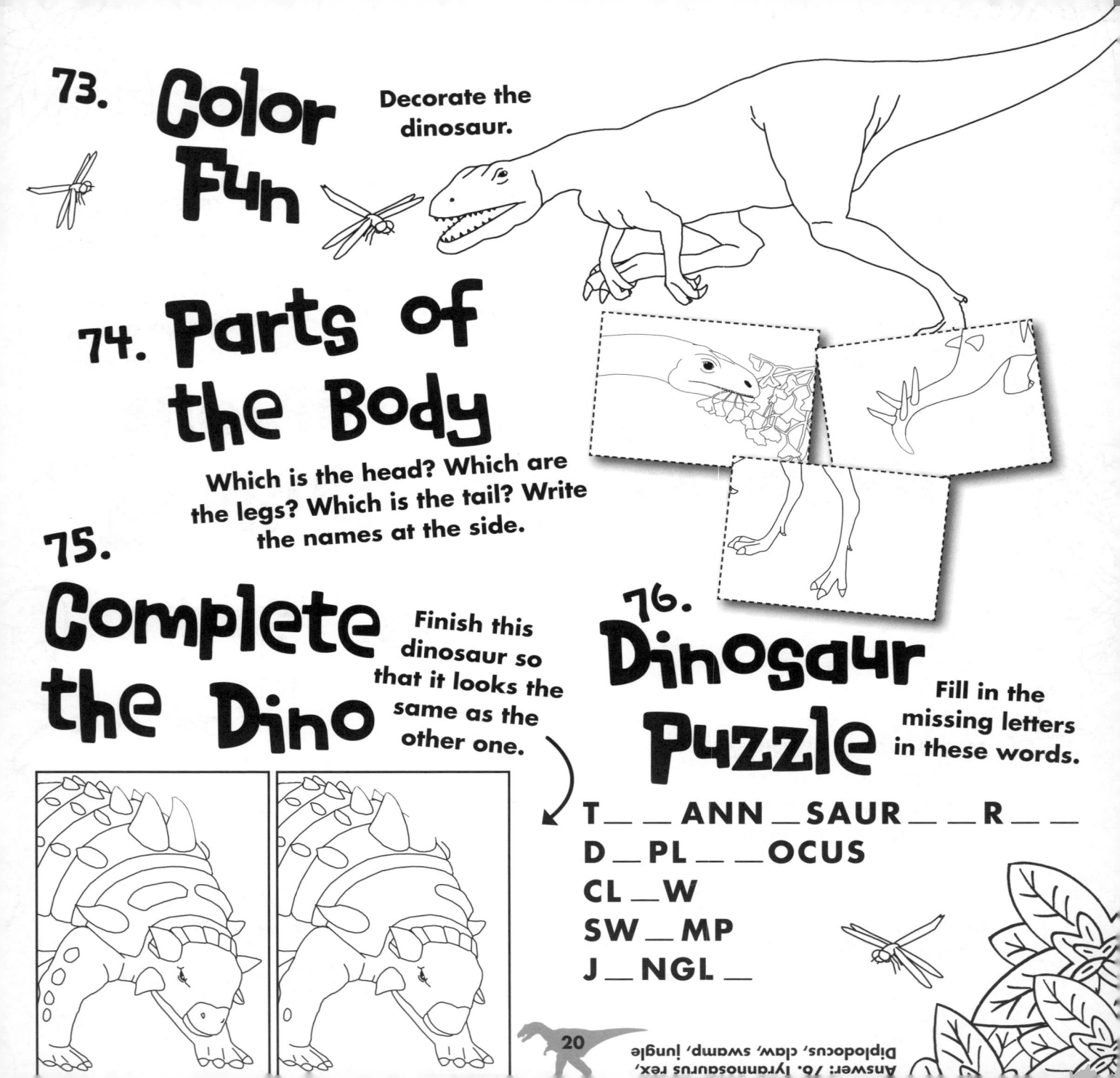

20

Answer: 76. tyrannosaurus rex, Diplodocus, claw, swamp, jungle

77. Dinosaur World

Draw the dinosaurs to complete this scene.

78. What's Happening?

Write a word or a sentence to describe the scene.

_____

_____

_____

_____

_____

79. Other Half

Draw the other half of this dinosaur.

80. Naming Dinosaurs

Name as many dinosaurs as you can in one minute. Get someone to time you!

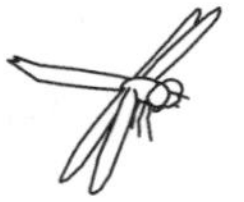

81. Matching

(7)
(2)

Match the pictures to their outlines.

(10)

82. Finishing Touches

Finish drawing the dinosaurs and color them.

(16)

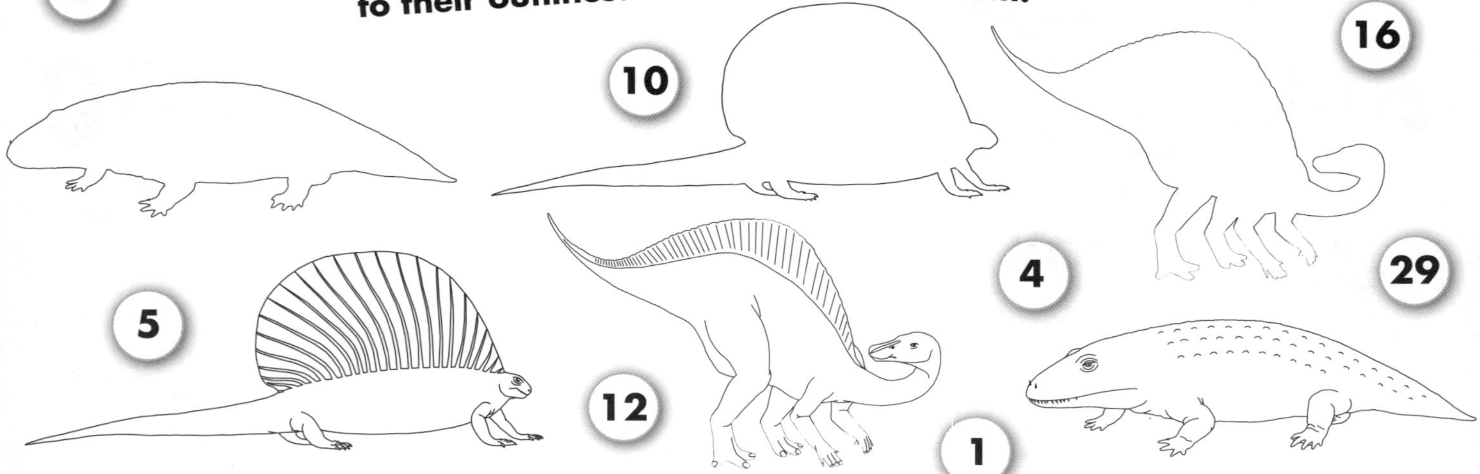

(4)

(29)

(5)

(12)

(1)

83. Stego Maths

(3)

(9)

Add all the numbers in circles on this page. What is the answer?

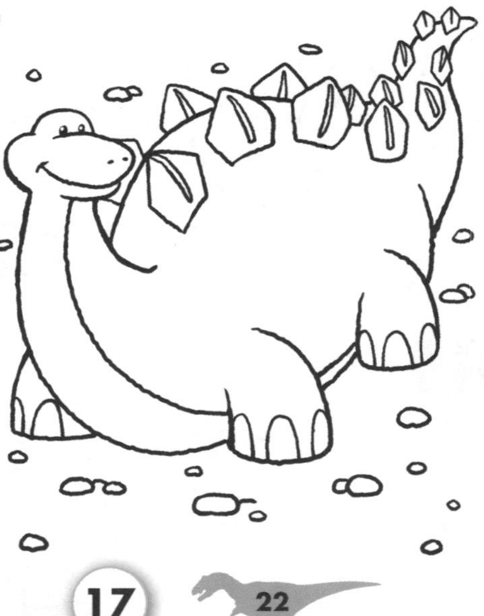

84. Making Words

How many words of 2 or more letters can you find in the word STEGOSAURUS? Write them in the box below.

(5)

(17)

22

85. Counting Dino Spikes

Can you count how many spikes this dinosaur has?

86. Spiky!

Color each of the spikes a different color.

87. Dragonfly Search

Can you find **10** dragonflies flying around this page?

88. Dinosaur Names

Do you know how to say the different dinosaur names? If you don't, ask a grown-up to help you.

Tyrannosaurus   **Oviraptor**
Triceratops   **Parasaurolophus**
Diplodocus   **Stegosaurus**

89. Matching Numbers

Draw a line to connect the prehistoric beasts with the same number.

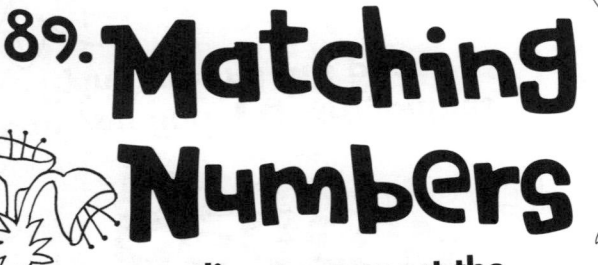

74

28

19

nineteen

twenty eight

seventy four

90. Colorful beasts

Draw matching patterns on the beasts with the same numbers.

91. Scrambled words

Unscramble the letters to spell out the names of things in the picture. Write the words on the lines.

onom	eerts
gesg	sagrs
tsen	ctyerodptal
oclud	raoflnndgy

92. Colorful Jungle

Color all the jungle plants on this page.

24

pterodactyl, cloud, dragonfly

93. Odd One Out

Draw a circle around the dinosaur that is different.

94. Dinosaur Model

Make a dinosaur model out of modeling clay. Make a ball for the body and a ball for the head. Roll a long neck, tail and four thick legs. Stick it all together and have fun!

95. Busy Dinosaurs

Color the spaces with *dino* written on them green. Color the spaces with *saur* written on them brown.

96. What Is Happening in the Picture?

Write a word or sentence to describe what is happening.

_____

_____

25

97. Word Search

Can you find these dinosaur names in the grid?

Tyrannosaurus   **Plateosaurus**

Spinosaurus   **Triceratops**

X	S	A	B	M	V	C	X	L	K	T	T	S
H	J	F	F	G	H	J	O	L	H	Y	U	H
M	S	T	T	T	T	P	K	P	R	J	H	
N	B	P	E	E	E	Y	H	U	A	S	S	
V	E	I	Q	Q	X	A	A	N	A	W		
W	T	N	T	S	A	R	N	Y	N			
W	H	Y	O	R	P	C	O	B	Y			
A	E	I	S	T	G	S	R	W				
X	G	H	J	T	K	P	J	A	Y	A	O	K
C	A	K	A	A	L	V	E	B	U	U	O	O
L	K	L	L	G	J	H	T	E	R	R	B	I
J	P	V	C	R	E	T	K	A	Y	U	U	C
T	R	I	C	E	R	O	T	O	P	S	P	S

98. Different Foods

What might these prehistoric beasts eat? If it eats plants draw a leaf beside it. If it eats meat draw a bone beside it. → If it eats fish draw a fish beside it. →

99. Connect the dots

Connect the dots from a to z to complete the picture.

100. Color it

Color the picture.

101. Who Goes Where?

Draw a line from each prehistoric beast to the word that describes where it spends the day.

Land   Sea   Sky

102. Fly Away!

Draw your own flying reptile.

103. Dinosaur Sentences

Finish these sentences by unscrambling the words from the boxes below.

The dinosaur went to _ _ _. EBD

T-rex ate an _ _ _. GEG

Diplodocus was _ _ _. ASD

Brachiosarus closed one _ _ _. YEE

104. Make Believe

Pretend that you are a huge dinosaur, and do the things described in each sentence. Remember to do it the way a dinosaur would.

27

Answer: 103. Bed, egg, sad, eye

105. Spot the Difference

Look carefully at the two pictures. How many differences can you find in the picture on the right?

107. What Can You See?

Write down the names of things in the picture. Write the words on the lines.

_____

_____

106. Complete This Sentence:

I found ____ differences in the picture.

108. Colour it All!

28

109. Mothers and Babies

Oviraptor is very proud of her eggs, but she is not sure how many there are. Can you help her count them?

110. What Color?

What color do you think Oviraptor should be? Color her.

112. Coloring in

Color in the picture below.

111. Baby Dinosaurs

Match the egg halves to spell out the baby dinosaurs' names.

Pe

Ch

ris

vid

ily

Em

Da

ter

Sa

lly

29

113. Can You Label the Parts of This Dinosaur?

114. Funky Dinosaur

Color the different parts of the dinosaur in different colors.

115. The Angry Dinosaur

Put these sentences in the right order so the story makes sense.

○ A big crack appeared.

○ The ground shook.

○ The dinosaur was cross.

○ The dinosaur fell in the crack.

○ He stamped his foot.

116. Let's Pretend!

Pretend you are the dinosaur in the story.

117.
Dinosaur Swamp

Look at the picture below. Then answer the questions by putting a check in the correct box.

Are the dinosaurs in the water?

| Yes | No |

Is it raining?

| Yes | No |

Do the dinosaurs look happy?

| Yes | No |

Are the dinosaurs the only creatures in the picture?

| Yes | No |

118.
Color By Numbers

Color in the picture using the color key.

1 = green
2 = yellow
3 = brown
4 = purple
5 = red
6 = orange
7 = blue

120. Velociraptor Maze

Help the Velociraptor make it through the maze of clouds.

START

FINISH

119. Making Words

How many words can you make using the letters in

Velociraptor?

31

121. Connect the dots

Connect the dots to see what the Ceresiosaurus has caught.

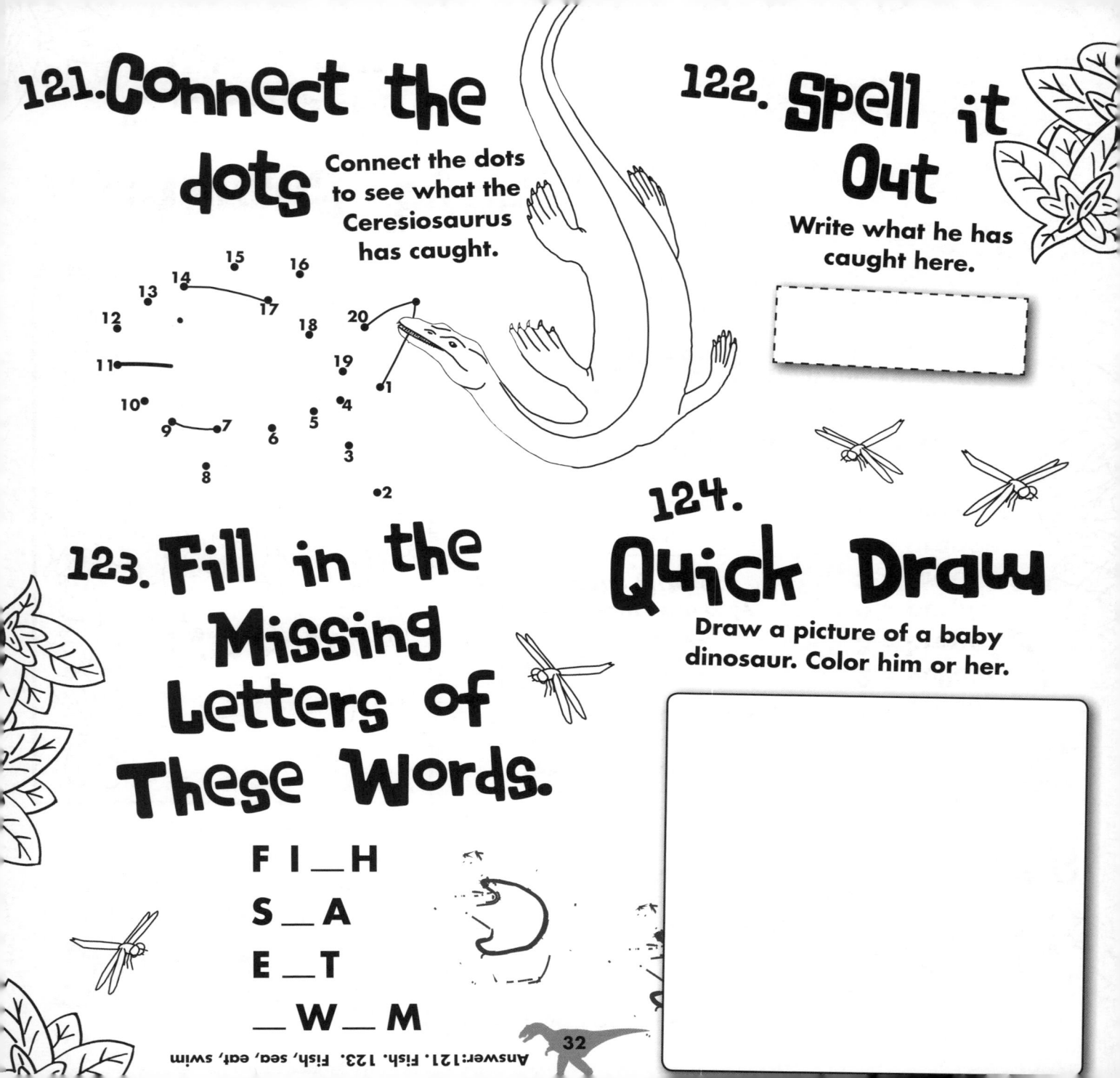

15 14 13 16 17 12 18 20 11 19 10 1 9 7 4 8 6 5 3 2

122. Spell it Out

Write what he has caught here.

123. Fill in the Missing Letters of These Words.

F I _ H

S _ A

E _ T

_ W _ M

124. Quick Draw

Draw a picture of a baby dinosaur. Color him or her.

125. Jurassic Scene

Look carefully at the picture. Can you see the things in the list below?

Something beginning with **F**.
Something that erupts beginning with **V**.
Something you can climb beginning with **T**.
Something on the dino's back beginning with **S**.

126. Coloring fun

Color the picture.

127. Dinosaur Math Puzzle

Multiply the number of long spikes this reptile has on his back by the number of legs he has. Write the answer in the box.

128. Color the dinosaur as brightly as you can.

33

129. Find the Dino

Write the first letter of each dinosaur's name. The letters below will help you.

P A T G

☐ yrannosaurus   ☐ patosarus

☐ rotoceratops   ☐ iganotosaurus

130. Same Sound

What other words can you think of beginning with these letters?

131. Prehistoric Math

Work out these problems. Write each answer in the box.

🦕🦕 − 🦎 = ☐

🦕🦕🦕🦕🦕 − 🦕🦕🦕 = ☐

🦖🦖 − 🦕🦕 = ☐

🦖🦖🦖 − 🦎 = ☐

🦕🦕 − 🦕🦕🦕 = ☐

132. Just Joking

Can you match each joke with its punch line?

A. Lazy bones

Q. What is T-rex's favorite number?

Q. What do you call a dino that won't get out of bed?

A. A Try-ceratops!

Q. What do you call a dinosaur that won't give up?

A. Eight (ate)

34

133. Spot the Difference

How many differences can you find between these 2 pictures?

134. Colorful scene

Color both pictures.

135. Word Search

Can you find these words in the word grid?
Draw a line through them as you find them.

Dinosaur, Fossil, Pterosaur, Bones, Shovel, Soil

F	O	S	S	I	L	G	O	S
B	A	C	D	J	B	R	J	O
O	T	L	I	A	P	F	Y	I
Y	B	O	N	E	S	S	L	L
P	A	B	O	E	N	S	E	H
J	N	S	H	O	V	E	L	P
U	O	Y	A	B	A	B	Y	L
P	A	T	U	E	N	M	E	N
P	T	E	R	O	S	A	U	R

136. More Words

What other words can you make from the letters in the grid?

35

Answer: 133. 4.

137. Fossil Maze

Pretend you're a fossil hunter and find a way through the maze to the dinosaur skull.

138. Skeleton Fun

Draw some bones on a piece of paper. Cut them out and make your own dinosaur skeleton.

139. Dotty

Connect the dots to reveal a hidden picture.

140. Dinosaur quiz

What is a fossil?
A type of food
An old man
Preserved remains of prehistoric beasts

What did T-Rex eat?
Grass
Meat
Cookies

What was a pterosaur?
A flying reptile
A nasty smell
A spelling mistake

prehistoric beasts, meat, a flying reptile

141. Vacation Plans

T-rex doesn't know what to take on vacation.
Rearrange the letters to reveal 5 things he needs.

oohhtbrtus

boko

asop

tshros

brea

142. Colourful Shirt

Draw in T-Rex's vacation shirt.
Give it a bright, summery design.

143. Different Dinos

Look at the dinosaur in each box. Draw an X next to the one that is different.

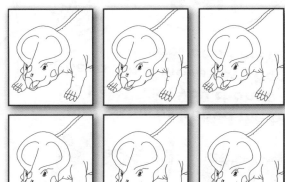

144. Dinosaur Stomp

Lots of dinosaurs had big, heavy feet. Make up a dinosaur dance by stomping your feet.

145. Word Ladder

Plateosaurus butted the ball with his head. Can you change "ball" to "head" in 5 moves by changing one letter at a time?

Ball
_ _ _ _
_ _ _ _
_ _ _ _
_ _ _ _
Head

146. Design a Jersey

Design a soccer jersey for Plateosaurus and his team.

147. Dinosaur Soccer

Arrange a soccer game with your friends, but pretend you are all dinosaurs when you play!

148. Team

Name the dinosaur soccer team!

38

149. Who is this?

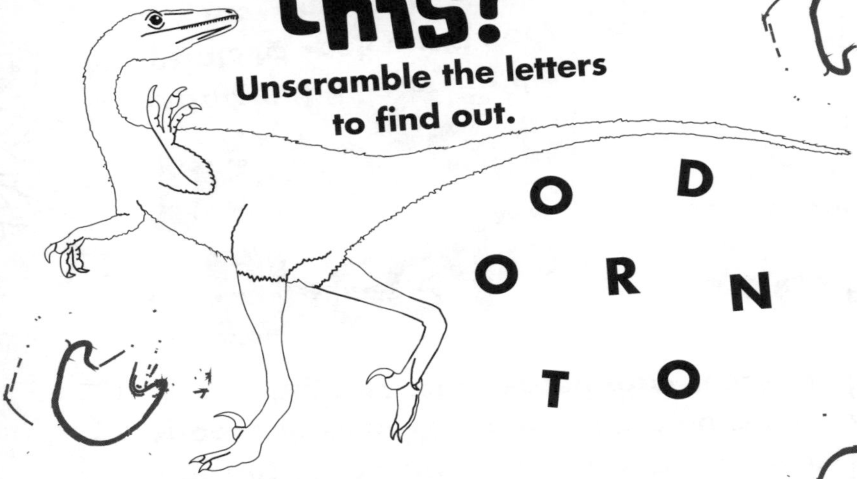

Unscramble the letters to find out.

O D
O R N
T O

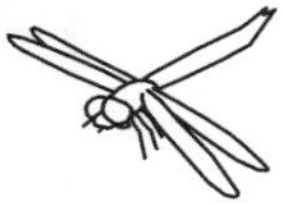

150. Which dinosaur is this?

Stegoceras?
Tyrannosaurus rex?
Triceratops?

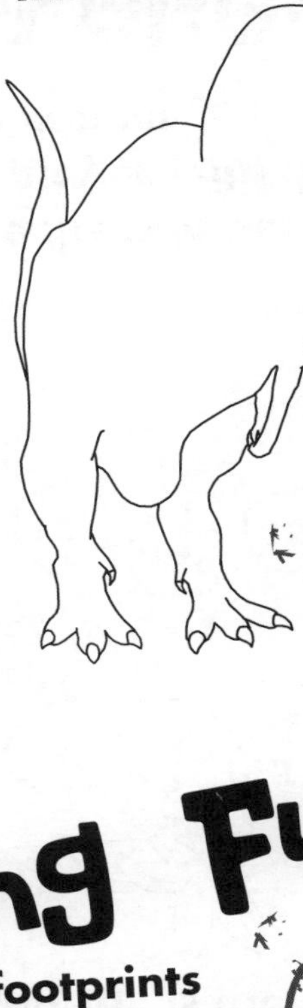

151. Fill in the Missing Letters of These Words.

E _ G
F _ _ T P R I _ T
L _ A V _ S
R _ _ R

152. Coloring Fun

Color all the footprints and leaves on the page.

39

153. Dinosaur Race

Have a race with a friend. Start at the "start" line. Take turns throwing a dice and move the number of footprints shown. The first player to reach the "finish" is the winner.

START FINISH

154. Highest Score

Starting at the start line, take turns throwing a dice. Move the number of spaces shown. Write down the number you land on. The player with the highest score when they cross the finish line is the winner.

155. Speedy Dinosaur

Unscramble the letters in the footprints to spell out a very fast dinosaur.

l r o e r a
c v i t o p

156. Make-believe

If you were a dinosaur, which one would you be? Draw a picture of what you might look like if you were a dinosaur.

157. Dino Snacks

Look carefully at all the things in the dino's lunchbox. Now cover them up and see if you can remember them all.

158. Who Am I?

Can you guess who I am?

I am a gentle plant eater.

I am very long.

I have a long tail that I use to whip enemies.

I swallow stones to grind up food in my tummy.

My name begins with D and ends in S.

159. Brighten the Scene!

Color the picture as neatly as you can!

160. Dinosaur Vowels

This dinosaur name has lost all its vowels. Can you put them back in to reveal what it is?

vowels ⟶ A E I O U

_ D M _ N T _ S A _ R _ S

Answer: 158. Diplodocus. 160. Edmontosaurus

161. Thumping Footprints

How many dinosaur footprints can you spot in this picture?

How many dragonflies can you find around the page? Ring them.

162. Picture Search

163. Whose Tail?

Match each dinosaur with its tail.

164. Dinosaur Knowledge

Decide whether these sentences are true or false.
Put a check ✓ in the yes or no box.

	yes	no
All dinosaurs had 2 legs.	☐	☐
Dinosaurs were giant lizards.	☐	☐
Dinosaurs ate human beings.	☐	☐
Dinosaurs lived millions of years ago.	☐	☐
The word *dinosaur* means "terrible lizard."	☐	☐

42

165. Spiny Dinosaur

Join the letters from a–z to see who is hiding in the jungle.

166. Who Am I?

Do you know the name of this dinosaur (above)? Here are some clues. →

He had a big sail on his back.

He was a meat-eater.

His name begins with **S** and ends with **S**.

167. Wordchain

Find 4 dinosaur names in the wordchain. Then write them on the footprints.

artlesapatosaurusgstrprotoceratopsltrstystegosaurusuvxyytriceratops

168. Dinosaur Jumble

Rearrange these letters to find the name of a dinosaur with a hard head.

SACERGOETS

Answer: 166. Spinosaurus. 167. Apatosaurus, Protoceratops, Stegosaurus, Triceratops. 168. Stegoceras.

169. Dinosaur Dinner

Unscramble the letters to spell out the names of things in the picture. Write the words on the lines.

ihfs
_ _ _ _

lspsah
_ _ _ _ _ _

wigns
_ _ _ _ _

antpl
_ _ _ _ _

aterw
_ _ _ _ _

doptenoran
_ _ _ _ _ _ _ _ _

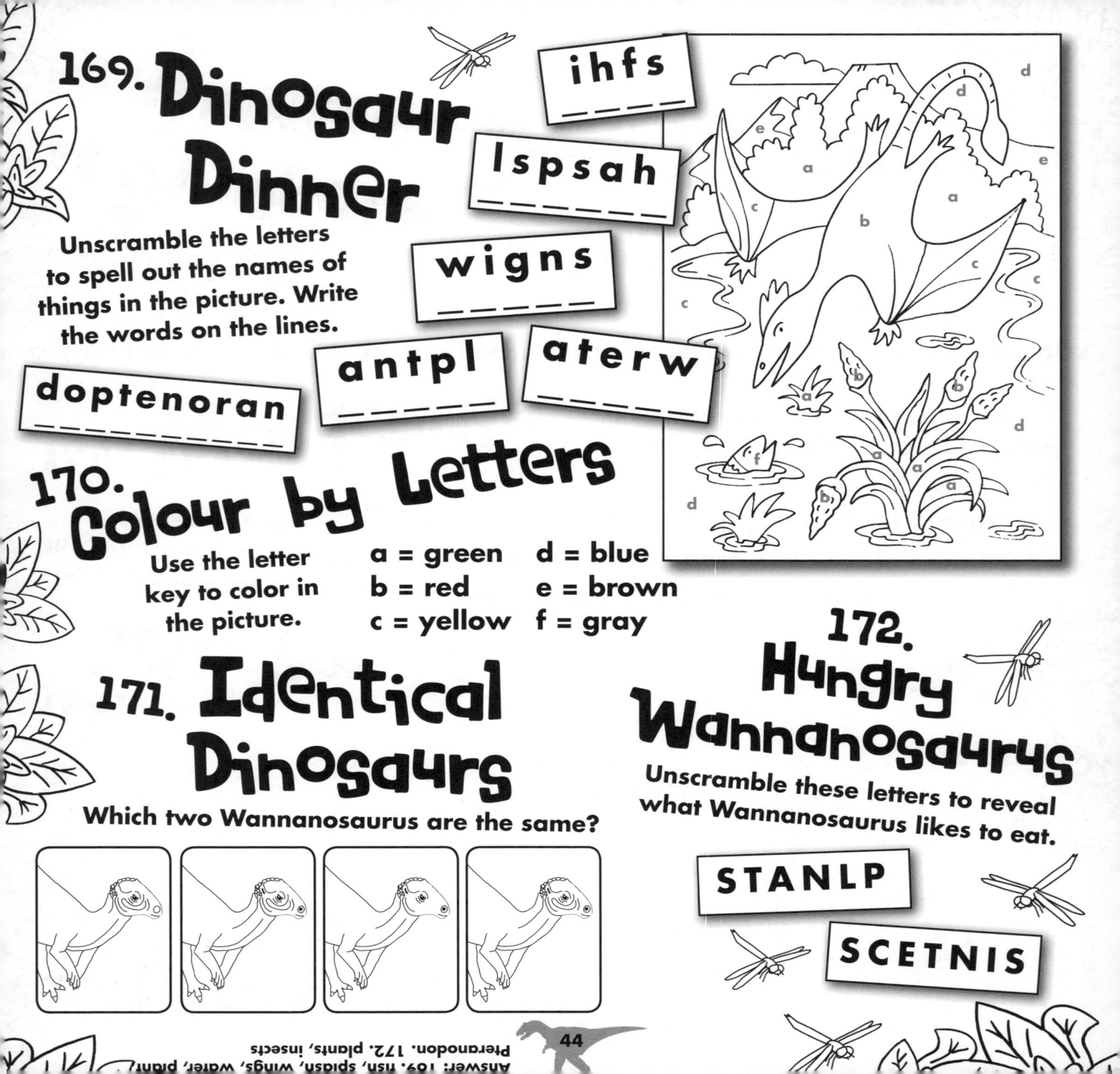

170. Colour by Letters

Use the letter key to color in the picture.

a = green   d = blue
b = red   e = brown
c = yellow f = gray

171. Identical Dinosaurs

Which two Wannanosaurus are the same?

172. Hungry Wannanosaurus

Unscramble these letters to reveal what Wannanosaurus likes to eat.

STANLP

SCETNIS

44

173. Gentle Giants

Dinosaurs lived millions of years ago. Can you see what doesn't belong in this prehistoric picture?

174. Coloring fun

Color the picture.

175. Dinosaur Grid

Can you find these dinosaurs in the word grid?

Coelurus, Velociraptor, Allosaurus, Spinosaurus, Tyrannosaurus, Ornithomimus, Oviraptor, Plateosaurus, Diplodocus, Apatosaurus, Brachiosaurus, Iguanodon.

S	P	I	N	O	S	A	U	R	U	S	E	E
V	E	L	O	C	I	R	A	P	T	O	R	R
O	R	N	I	T	H	O	M	I	M	U	S	R
P	L	A	T	E	O	S	A	U	R	U	S	T
P	A	B	O	I	G	U	A	N	O	D	O	N
J	N	K	C	O	E	L	U	R	U	S	P	P
U	O	Y	D	I	P	L	O	D	O	C	U	S
A	P	A	T	O	S	A	U	R	U	S	N	N
P	A	L	L	O	S	A	U	R	U	S	S	R
B	R	A	C	H	I	O	S	A	U	R	U	S
T	Y	R	A	N	N	O	S	A	U	R	U	S
P	T	E	O	V	I	R	A	P	T	O	R	R

176. Extreme Dinosaurs

How much do you know about dinosaurs? Answer these questions to find out.

a. Which was the biggest dinosaur?
b. Which was the biggest meat-eating dinosaur?
c. Can you name the smallest dinosaur?
d. Can you name the longest dinosaur?

45

Answer: 176. Argentinosaurus, Giganotosaurus, Microraptor, Seismosaurus

46

177. Busy Babies

How many dinosaur babies can you count?

178. Colourful Characters

Color the babies lots of different colors.

179. Shadows

Look at each prehistoric beast and draw around the correct shadow.

180. Who Am I?

I am a huge plant-eating dinosaur beginning with the letter A. I used to live in Argentina.

Write my name here:

_____

181. Missing Words

Polly Protoceratops has gotten an invitation but some of the words have been replaced by pictures. Look at the pictures and write each word in the space above.

Dear Polly,

Please come to my party in the

 _ _ _ _ _ _ circle near my cave,

tomorrow at set.

Be there or be _ _ _ _ _ _ _ .

Be there or be

Love, Sally Stegosaurus

182. Dinosaur Party

Why don't you ask if you can have a dinosaur party? You could send out dinosaur invitations, wear dinosaur masks, play dinosaur games, and eat dinosaur snacks.

183. Dinosaur Mask

Ask a grown-up to help you make a dinosaur mask out of 2 paper plates. Draw big eyes on one plate and cut them out. Stick them to the top of the other plate. Draw on nostrils and big scary teeth. Stick on horns, brows, and frills. Make a hole on two sides and thread a string through to fasten it to your head. Grrrr!

184. Dino Egg Hunt

Get a grown-up to cut out lots of dinosaur eggs. You can decorate them if you like. Hide the eggs around the house or yard and get all your friends to hunt for them. Everyone who finds 5 eggs gets a prize.

185. Happy Homes

Follow the line each Sordes has made with a different colored pen to find out where they live.

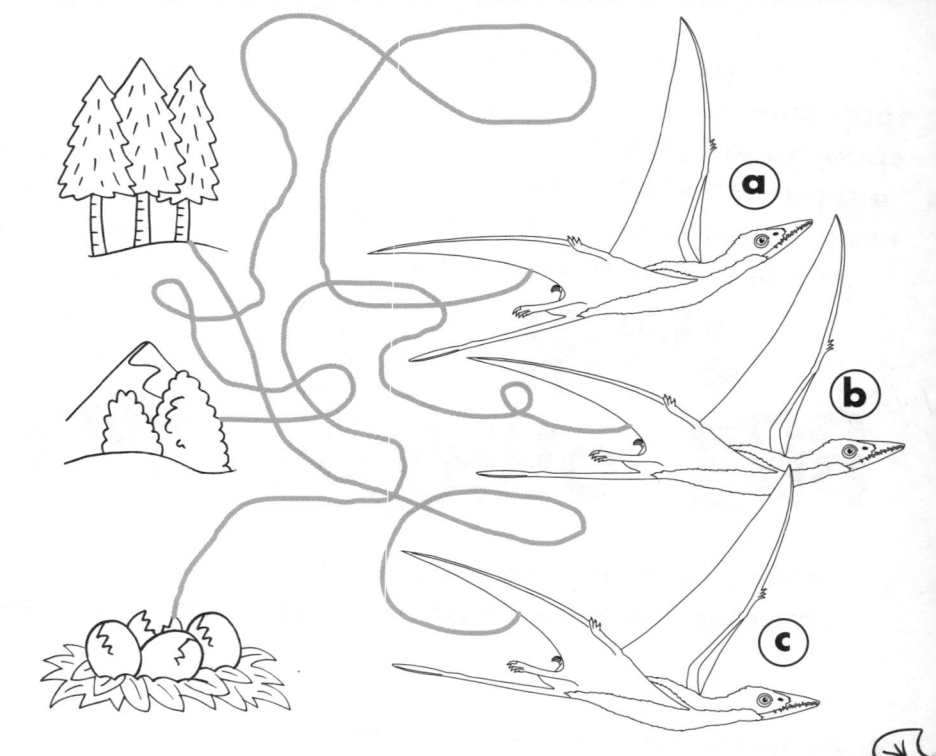

186. Pretty Sordes

Color in Sordes.

187. Squawk like a Sordes

What sound do you think a Sordes would make? Flap your wings and squawk like a Sordes!

188. Dinosaur Movies

Unscramble the letters to find the names of 2 famous dinosaur movies.

SAURDIONS

SSICARUJ RKPA

48

189. The Same

Color the 2 in each row that are exactly the same.

190. Different Dinosaurs

Think of a dinosaur beginning with these letters. Write its name beside the correct letter.

T

I

P

R

S

191. Design a Dino

Draw your own pet dinosaur in this box!

192. Mirror Writing

Somebody has written these dinosaur names backward. Can you sort them out?

CAPTOSAURUS

MEGALOSAURUS

DEINONYCHUS

Answer: 192. Captosaurus, Megalosaurus, Deinonychus

193. Finish the Dino

Draw the other half of this dinosaur.

195. Growing Up

Copy the smaller dinosaur picture into the bigger grid.

194. What Next?

Make up a story about this dinosaur and what happens during its day!

196. Missing Vowels

This dinosaur name has lost all its vowels. Put in the correct vowels to see the name.

vowels → A E I O U

SP_N_S__R_S

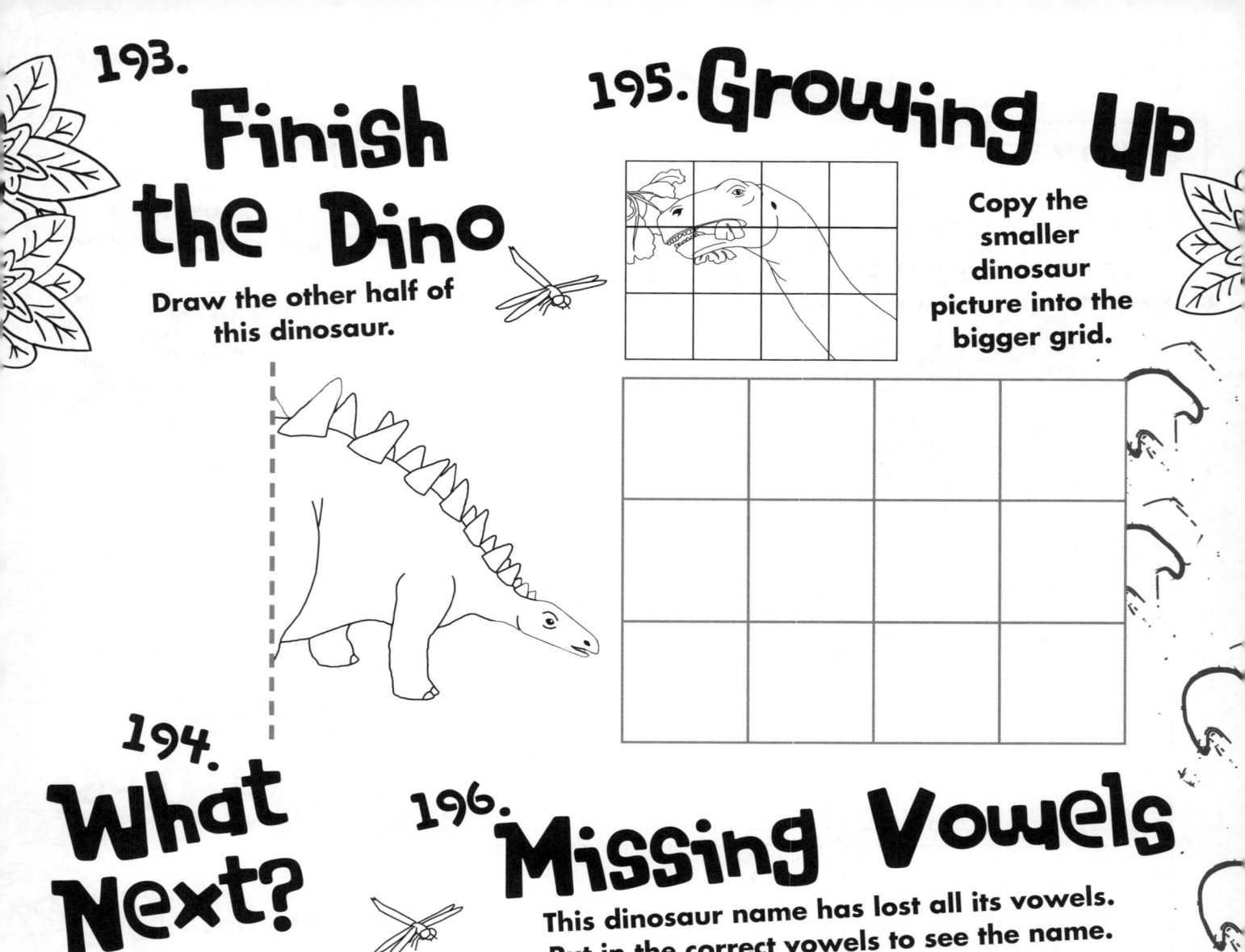

50

19. Necks and Tails

Play this game with up to 4 friends. Put a counter on "Start" and take turns throwing a dice. Move the number of spaces shown. If you land on a neck, slide up the board. If you land on a tail, slide down. The first player to reach "Home" is the winner.

25	26	27	28	29	Home
24	23	22	21	20	19
13	14	15	16	17	18
12	11	10	9	8	7
Start	2	3	4	5	6

198. Find the Dinosaur

Find the dino hiding on this page.

199. Dinosaur Discovery

How many dinosaur bones can you find?

200. Quick Question

A paleontologist is:

A plant expert.
A very pale expert.
A fossil expert.

201. Bones

Copy the bone shapes from this page and cut them out. Make two sets.
Put the bones in a pile and take it in turns with your friend throwing a dice. If you throw an even number, pick up a bone.
Continue until all the bones are gone.

202. Color It

Color each dinosaur bone a different colour.

203.
Reptile Dreams

What is this reptile dreaming about? Connect the dots to find out.

204.
Bring it to Life

Color the dreaming reptile.

205.
Missing

Fill in the missing letters in these words.

F _ R N
S K _ _ L
D R E _ M
S K _ L _ T _ N

206.
Think of other words that begin with the first letters of these words.

Answer: 205. Fern, skull, dream, skeleton

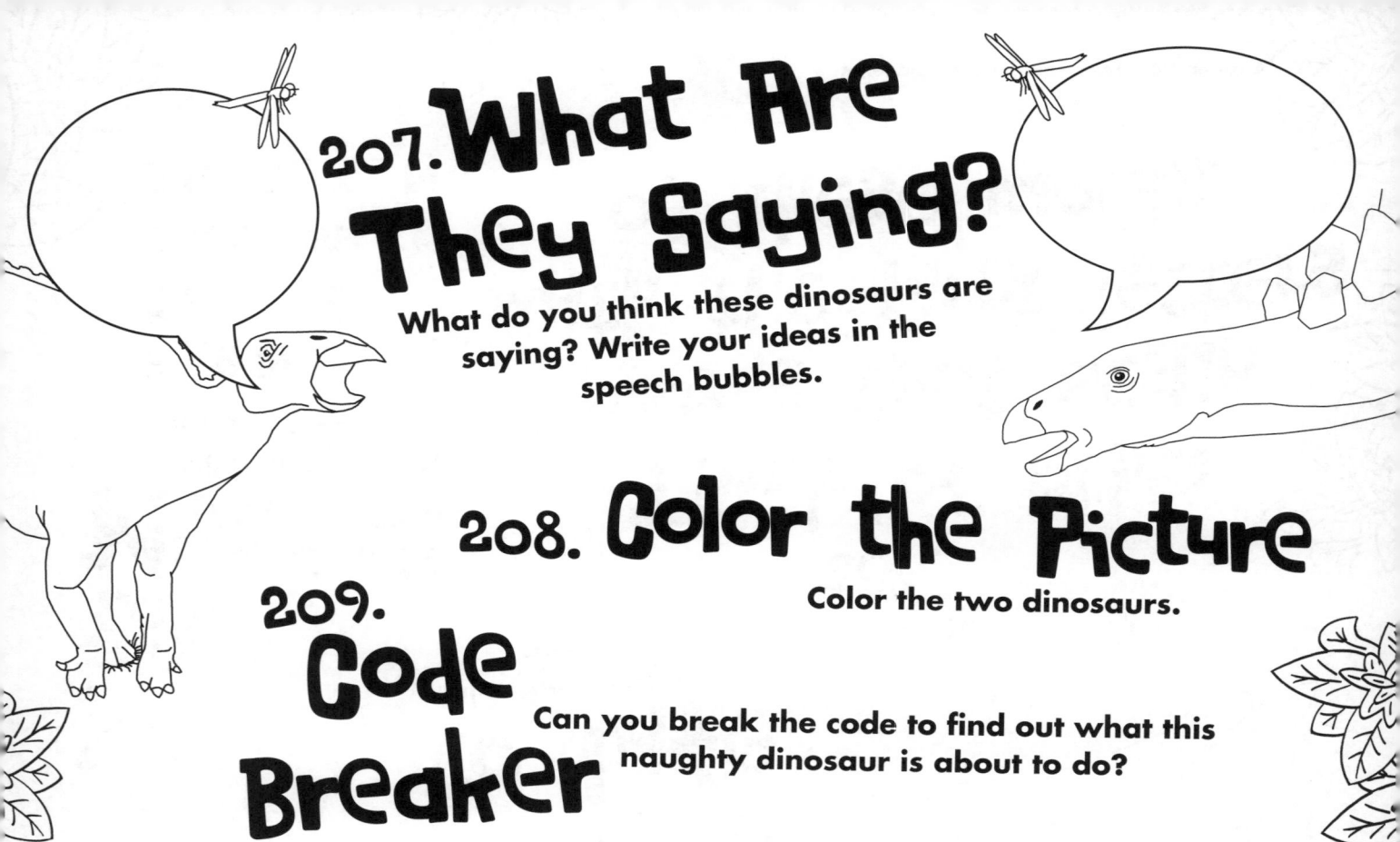

207. What Are They Saying?

What do you think these dinosaurs are saying? Write your ideas in the speech bubbles.

208. Color the Picture

Color the two dinosaurs.

209. Code Breaker

Can you break the code to find out what this naughty dinosaur is about to do?

1=a	2=b	3=c	4=d	5=e	6=f	7=g	8=h	9=i	10=j	11=k	12=l	13=m	14=n
15=o	16=p	17=q	18=r	19=s	20=t	21=u	22=v	23=w	24=x	25=y	26=z		

16 12 1 25   19 15 3 3 5 18   23 9 20 8   20 8 5   5 7 7
___ ___ ___ ___ ___ ___ ___ ___ ___ ___ ___ ___ ___ ___ ___ ___ ___ ___ ___

210. Dino Decode

Use the same code to work out what this says.

14 15   4 9 14 15 19 1 21 18 19
___ ___ ___ ___ ___ ___ ___ ___ ___ ___ ___

211. Square Deal

Redraw the squares in the correct order to reveal a spiny dinosaur.

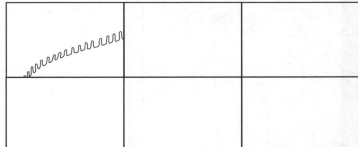

212. Coloring Fun

Color the picture.

213. Right Path

To get home safely, the little dinosaur needs to go past 2 trees, 1 mountain, and the dinosaur burial ground. Which path should he take?

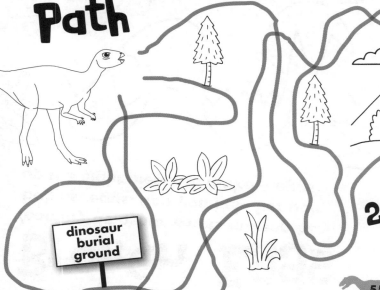

HOME

dinosaur burial ground

214. Jumbled Giant

Rearrange these letters to spell out a giant dinosaur.

RBAHCOISAURSU

55

215.
Broken Eggs

Mommy dinosaur wants to keep her babies' eggs. Can you help her pair up the eight pieces to make 4 eggs?

216. Broken Words

Can you join up these letters to make dinosaur names?

DIPLO	OMIMUS
ORNITH	ODON
OVI	DOCUS
IGUAN	SAURUS
TYRANNO	RAPTOR

217. Find the Difference

Can you find 6 differences between these 2 pictures?

218.
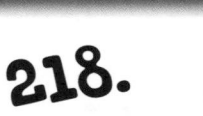
Color Them

Color both pictures, making them as different as possible.

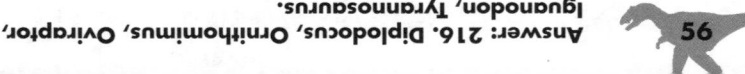

Answer: 216. Diplodocus, Ornithomimus, Oviraptor, Iguanodon, Tyrannosaurus.

56

219. Fishing Fun

Which fish has the reptile caught?

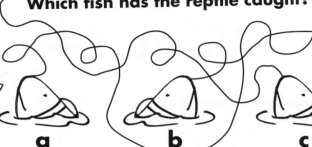

a   b   c   d

220. Dinosaur Names

Dinosaurs are often named after the places their fossils have been found. Where do you think these dinosaurs come from?

Argentinosaurus
Lesothosaurus
Indosaurus

221. I Spy

How many things beginning with **T** can you see in this picture?

222. Memory Game

Look very carefully at the picture. Then cover it up and answer these questions.

How many T-rexes are there?
What is in the sky?
How many flowers are there?

57

223. Story Time

Make up a story about this scene.

224. Happy Ending

Now color the picture.

225. Scrambled Words

Unscramble the letters to spell out the names of things in the picture. Write the words on the lines.

t c o o c n u
_ _ _ _ _ _ _

f o t o
_ _ _ _

t e h e t
_ _ _ _ _

u c l o d
_ _ _ _ _

r u t n k
_ _ _ _ _

226. To Begin

Look at the picture again. Say each thing you can see. Can you think of other words that begin with each of the beginning sounds?

Answer: 225. coconut, foot, teeth, cloud, trunk

227. Dinosaur Knowledge

Decide whether these sentences are true or false. Put a check ✓ in the yes or no box.

	yes	no
Dinosaurs lived for over 85 million years.	☐	☐
Dinosaurs are still alive today.	☐	☐
Some dinosaurs were the size of chickens.	☐	☐
All dinosaurs were green.	☐	☐

228. Quick Quiz

What was a Protosuchus?

**A prehistoric cat
An early crocodile
A nasty cough**

229. Missing Things

The artist has forgotten some things in this picture. Can you put them in?

230. Coloring fun

Color in the pictures using the letter key.

a = green   d = yellow
b = red   e = brown
c = blue

Answer: 227. yes, no, yes, no.
228. An early crocodile

231. Dotty Fun

Connect the dots to see what the dinosaur is doing.

8
7
9
6
10
5
11
4
12
13
3
2
14
1
15

233. Poster Quiz

Look at this poster. Then answer the questions.

What is the play called?
Where is it being performed?
What date is it on?
What time does it start?

234. Poster Fun

Design your own dinosaur poster. It can be for any event you like, even your birthday party!

232. Missing Letters

Fill in the missing letters to reveal the name of the dinosaur in the balloon.

S L R S L

| A | _ | _ | O | _ | A U | _ | U | _ |

Prehistoric
by
Dina Saw

February 10 from 3-5 pm in the Town Hall

60

235. Word Ladder

Kannenmeyeria eats both roots and leaves. Can you change "leaf" to "root" by changing one letter at a time? These clues should help you.

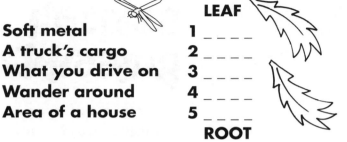

LEAF

Soft metal	1	_ _ _ _
A truck's cargo	2	_ _ _ _
What you drive on	3	_ _ _ _
Wander around	4	_ _ _ _
Area of a house	5	_ _ _ _

ROOT

236. Scrambled Word

Unscramble this word to find the name of a three-horned dinosaur.

R T C I R E T A P S O

_ _ _ _ _ _ _ _ _ _ _

238. Draw a Stegoceras's Bony Head!

237. Color the Kannenmeyeria and Leaves!

239. Dino Stats

Read about these dinosaurs. Then answer the questions below.

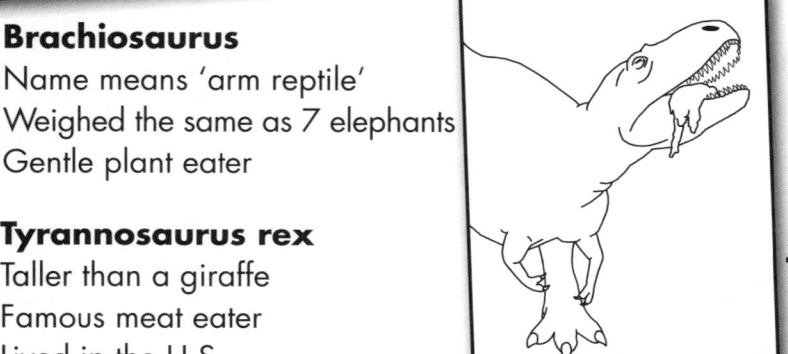

Brachiosaurus
Name means 'arm reptile'
Weighed the same as 7 elephants
Gentle plant eater

Tyrannosaurus rex
Taller than a giraffe
Famous meat eater
Lived in the U.S.

Whose name meant "arm reptile"?
Who was taller than a giraffe?
Who was a plant eater?
Who lived in the U.S.?

240. Picture This

Color the two dinos in the boxes.

241. Design Some Jerseys

These two dinosaurs are about to play soccer on opposite sides. Can you design a jersey for each of them?

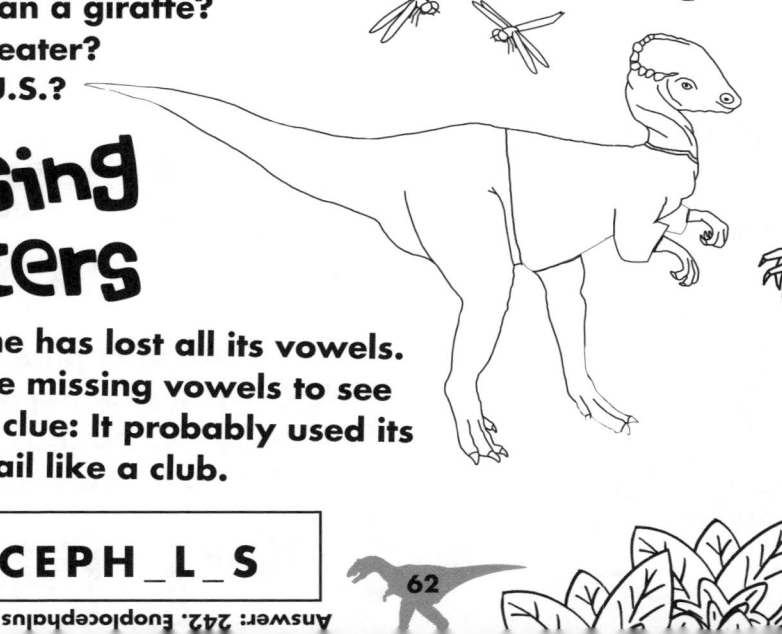

242. Missing Letters

This dinosaur name has lost all its vowels. Can you put in the missing vowels to see who it is? Here's a clue: It probably used its heavy tail like a club.

_ _ _ PL_CEPH_L_S

62

243. Dinosaur Hunter

Connect the dots to see what the dinosaur hunter has found.

244. Fun Words

Put these letters in the right order, and they will spell out something dinosaur experts look for.

SILSOF

245. Fun Today

Where can you go to see a fossil today? Unscramble these letters to find out.

SUMEMU

246. Hunting the Past

Pretend you are a dinosaur hunter. Make a list of all the equipment you would need.

247. Tell the Tale

Write some words or sentences describing what happens in a story about a dinosaur hunter.

_____

_____

_____

_____

63

251. Make the Same

Draw in the missing parts to make the two dinosaurs exactly the same.

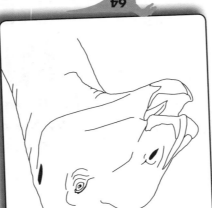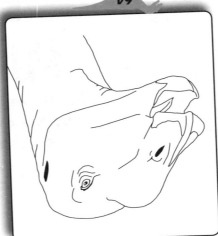

250. Find the Difference

Can you find 5 differences between these 2 dinosaurs?

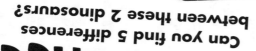

249. Color It

Color the dinosaur.

248. Dino Dots

Connect the dots to see what kind of tail this dinosaur has.

252. Color Codes

a = blue   c = yellow
b = green   d = red

Use the key to color the dinosaur pictures.

253. Finding Things

Can you find these things in the picture?

Snow   Palm tree
Mountains   Smile
Pool   Sky

254. Make a Copy

Copy the dinosaur into the grid and color it in.

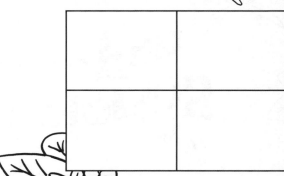

255. Sing-along

Dinosaurs haven't lived on earth for millions of years. Why do you think they disappeared? Maybe there was a huge volcanic explosion. Or maybe a big asteroid hit the earth. Make up a song or a poem about the last dinosaur.

65

256. Hunt the Dino

Can you find the dinosaur hiding in this picture?

257. Coloring Fun

Color in the scene.

258. Prehistoric Math

4	+ 2	= ___ rocks
4	x 6	= ___ Diplodocus
10	– 3	= ___ insects

260. Toothy

Draw a big dinosaur tooth!

259. More or fewer?

Does this dinosaur skull have more or fewer teeth than you do? Count them.

261. Pair Them Up

Draw a line between the two dinosaurs that are the same.

262. Color the Same

Color the matching dinosaurs the same color.

263. Walkies

Some prehistoric beasts walked on 4 legs. Some beasts walked on 2. Write 4 beside the beast that walked on 4 legs. Write 2 beside the beast that walked on 2 legs.

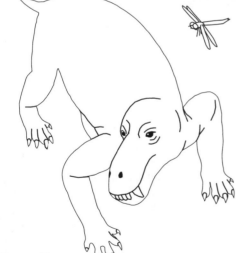

264. Coloring

Color the 4-legged dinosaur blue. Color the 2-legged dinosaur orange.

67

265. Shadowy Fun

Draw a line to match each shadow to its prehistoric creature.

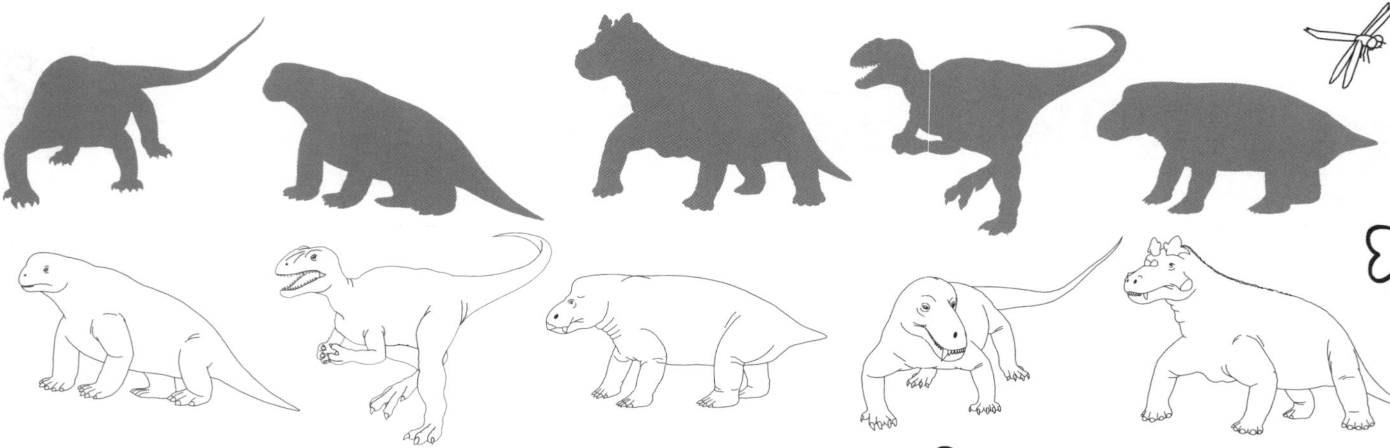

266. Shadow Puppet

Draw dinosaur shadows on paper and cut them out. Glue them to a lollipop or ice-cream stick. When it's dark, turn off the lights and shine a flashlight at a wall. Hold the puppets between the flashlight and the wall, and watch their shadows appear on the wall.

267. Decorate the Dinos

Decorate the dinosaurs above with colorful patterns and designs.

268. Counting Fun

Can you count how many flowers there are on this page?

269. Coloring Fun

Color each flower in a different pattern.

68

270.
Quiz Time

What did Diplodocus eat?
   Plants
   Chocolate
   Slugs

What was an Ichthyosaurus?
   A reptile that lived in the sea
   A dinosaur disease
   A dinosaur that lived in trees

271.
Underwater World

Draw waves and seaweed around the swimming reptile and on the rest of this page.

272.
Swimming!

How do you think Ichthyosaurus would swim? Pretend to swim like the beast all around the room!

273.
Tongue Twister

Try and say the name **Ichthyosaurus** out loud.

274. And Then...

Try and write **Ichthyosaurus** in the spaces below without looking at the spelling.

275. Dot-to-Dot

Connect the numbers in the correct order to finish the picture.

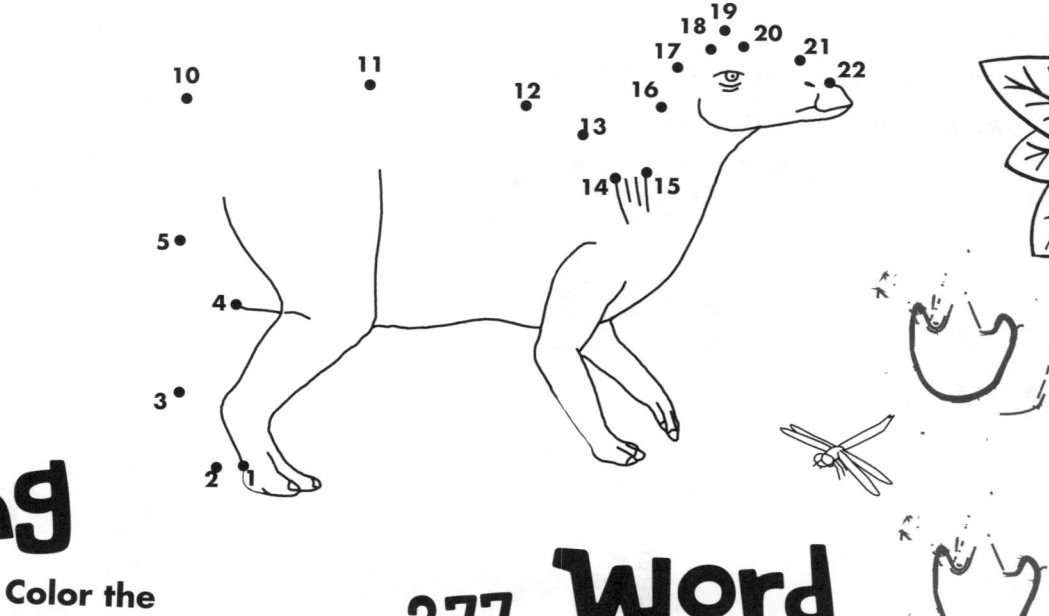

276. Coloring Fun

Color the dinosaur.

278. Opposites

Big is the opposite of small. Slow is the opposite of fast. Can you think of any other opposites?

277. Word Ladder

The big Diplodocus is slow. The little Velociraptor is fast. Change **SLOW** to **FAST** in seven moves by changing one letter at a time.

SLOW

1 _ _ _ _
2 _ _ _ _
3 _ _ _ _
4 _ _ _ _
5 _ _ _ _
6 _ _ _ _
7 _ _ _ _

FAST

279.
Angry Reptiles!

These two ocean-living reptiles are having a fight. What do you think they might be fighting about? Write it in the speech bubbles.

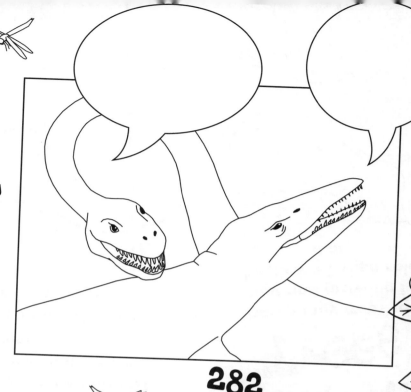

280.
Coloring Fun

Color the fighting dinosaurs.

281. First Letter

Camptosaurus begins with the letter **C**. Write down **5** other things that begin with the letter **C**.

_____
_____
_____
_____
_____

282.
Rhyming Words

Can you think of some things that rhyme with some of the things you found beginning with **C**? Write them here.

_____
_____
_____

283. Dinosaur Name

Unscramble the letters on this page to reveal the name of a dinosaur.

INIMM

284. D for Dinosaur

Dinosaur begins with the letter **D**. How many dinosaurs can you think of beginning with the letter **D**?

285. Which Way?

This dinosaur can't work out which is the quickest way to the lake. Can you help her figure it out following these clues?

It is the most winding path. It isn't the stoniest path. It is the path with the most trees.

286. Find the Trees

How many trees can you find growing in the picture? Then color it in.

72

287. True or False?

Eogyrinus hunted in the water.

288. Coloring Fun

Color the picture.

289. Mommy Maze

Which baby belongs to which mom?

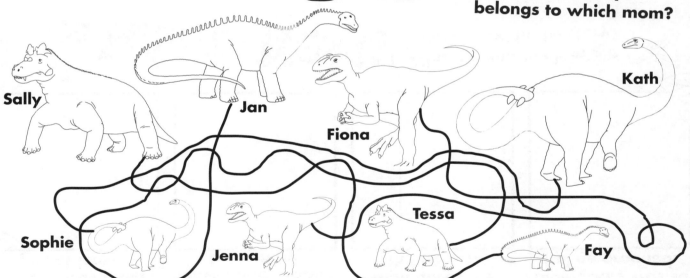

Sally

Jan

Fiona

Kath

Sophie

Jenna

Tessa

Fay

290. Story Time

Make up a story about one of the mom beasts and her baby.

73

291. Storyboard

Draw the pictures in the boxes to tell this story:

There was a big pile of leaves.	Diplodocus saw the leaves and rubbed his tummy.	Diplodocus ate the leaves.	Diplodocus was so full he groaned.

292. What Next?

What do you think might happen next in the story?

293. Making Bigger

294. Make Your Own Grid

Make the beast larger by copying her into the larger grid. We have started it for you.

Use a ruler to make your own grid on a sheet of paper. Find a dinosaur picture you want to copy and draw the same grid over it. Copy the dinosaur into your grid.

295. Who Is Hiding?

Shade in each section with a dot to reveal a hidden picture.

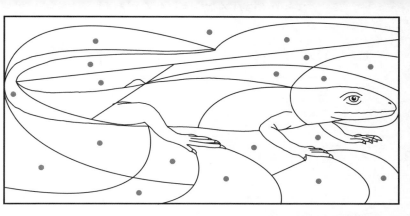

296. Alive Today?

What modern-day animal does this prehistoric beast look like?

297. Jumbled Letters

Rearrange the letters to spell out what the dinosaur is standing in.

dopn

298. Coloring Time

Color the picture using the key below.

1 = blue   4 = yellow
2 = brown   5 = red
3 = green

75

299. Copy the Beast

Copy this prehistoric beast in the space below it and color it.

300. Sing!

This dinosaur is called Seymour. Make up a song about him!

302. Different Colors

Color the leaves green. Color the footprints brown. Color the dinosaurs red.

301. Happy Dinosaurs

Draw some things that would make a grumpy dinosaur happy.

303. Little Leaves

The dinosaur can only step on leaves that spell out the name of something you use to write with. Color in the letters as you go. We have found the first letter for you.

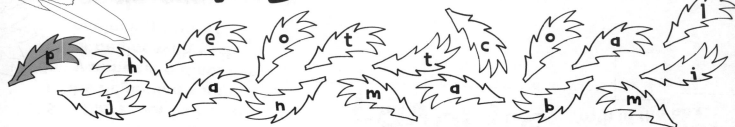

304. Hidden Words

Can you find these words hidden in the leaves?

top   jam   hat   boat

305. Dinosaur Jigsaw Puzzle

Which three of these jigsaw pieces complete the picture?

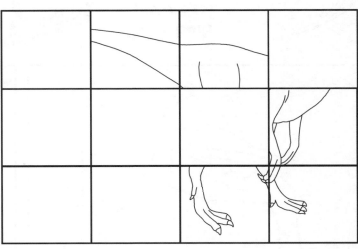

306. Finish It

77

Draw in the missing bits. Then color the picture.

307. Find the Difference

Can you find 4 differences between these 2 pictures?

308. Coloring Fun

Color both pictures.

309. A Is For...

Say these words. Listen to the beginning sound. Can you name a dinosaur that begins with each beginning sound?

apple, egg, house, mouse, ring, lizard, kite

310. Firm Favorite

Draw a picture of your favorite dinosaur and write the letter it begins with in the box.

2
3

311. Finding Words

Can you find at least three words of three letters or more in the word MEGALOSAURUS? Write them in the Megalosaurus.

6

4

7

312. Drawing Fun

Draw your own picture of a Tyrannosaurus here. Then color it.

15 **14**

313. Desert Fun

Help the dinosaur cross the scorching desert. He can only step on stones that have even numbers on them.

9

11

5

1

8

13

314. Odd or Even

Color all the even-numbered stones red. Color all the odd-numbered stones blue.

12

16

Answer: 317. Massive, loud, extinct, amazing!

317. Dinosaur Puzzle

Fill in the missing letters to find words that describe dinosaurs.

M_SSIV_

L_UD

EXT_ _C_

AM _ZI_ _!

316. Color It

Color the correct mirror image.

318. Make a Jigsaw Puzzle

With the help of a grown-up, look for a dinosaur picture in an old comic book or on the internet. Glue it to cardboard and divide it into pieces with a pencil. Then cut out the pieces. Have fun putting it together again and again.

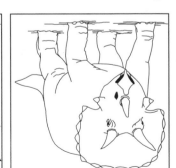

315. Looking Pretty

Can you find the first dinosaur's mirror image?

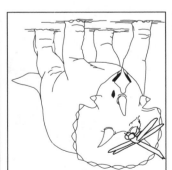

319. Complete the Cartoon

The artist has forgotten to add the dinosaurs to this cartoon scene. Can you add them for him?

320. What's Happening?

Write a word or a sentence to describe the scene.

321. Other Half

Draw the other half of this roaring dinosaur.

322. Naming Dinosaurs

Name as many meat-eating dinosaurs as you can in one minute.

323. Disappearing Dinosaurs

Look at these two pictures. Some things have disappeared from the second picture. Can you see what is missing?

324. Put Them Back

Can you put the missing things back into the second picture?

325. Quick Quiz

Answer yes or no to these questions by putting a check in the correct box.

	yes	no
Dinosaurs are extinct.	◯	◯
Dinosaurs lived on the moon.	◯	◯
Dinosaurs laid eggs.	◯	◯
Dinosaurs had 6 legs.	◯	◯

326. Spelling

Write these dinosaur names a couple of times on a piece of paper. Once you think you have learned how to spell them, test yourself!

Lufengosaurus   Deinocheirus
Maiasaura   Sellosaurus

82

Answer 325. Yes, no, yes, no.

327. Dividing Patterns

Color and draw different patterns on each half of this strange prehistoric creature!

328. Making Words

How many words beginning with D can you find in the word DEINONYCHUS? Write them in the box below.

329. Find the Bones

Can you find 10 bones hidden around the page?

330. Coloring Fun

Color in the picture.

331. Find the Ball

Draw a line between each prehistoric beast and the ball with the same number.

three

one

two

3

2   1

332. Color to match

Color the dinosaurs and their balls the same color.

334. Poem

Make up a poem with these words.

333. Scrambled Words

Unscramble the letters to spell out words. Write the words on the lines.

SPOTARECIRT

_____

LYTCADORETP

_____

ELITPER

_____

335. Odd One Out

Draw a circle around the odd one out.

336. Make the Same

Draw in the missing parts to make the odd one out the same as the others.

337. Dinosaur Prints

Ask an adult to cut a potato in half. Draw a dinosaur footprint on the cut part of one potato. Then ask an adult to cut it out so you have a potato stamp. Dip the stamp in paint and make potato prints on a sheet of paper. You could make your own wrapping paper.

338. Foot Dinosaur

Put your foot on a sheet of paper and draw around it. Use this footprint to create a Stegosaurus. The heel end is the head and the toe end is the body. Add a tail and cut out triangles of paper for the back plates. Draw on legs, feet, eyes, and mouth.

339. What's Up?

Look carefully at the picture. Then answer these questions.

1. What is the spiky dinosaur standing in?

2. How many leaves are on the tree?

3. How many dinosaurs are there?

4. What is the name of the dinosaur that is farthest away?

340. Wordsearch

Can you find these dinosaur names in the grid?

Tyrannosaurus, Spinosaurus, Plateosaurus, Triceratops
Coelurus, Velociraptor, Allosaurus,

T	S	S	C	X	L	U	U	L	A	E	A	Y
R	Y	U	K	O	Q	P	H	J	K	L	L	M
I	Z	R	J	V	E	V	P	V	L	N	L	S
C	M	U	A	I	E	L	C	X	K	J	O	U
E	P	A	C	N	N	L	U	H	G	F	S	R
R	A	S	O	A	N	H	C	R	D	S	A	U
A	N	O	E	Q	C	O	G	I	U	A	U	A
T	B	N	L	V	B	Y	S	E	R	S	R	S
O	C	I	U	B	E	R	F	A	E	E	U	O
P	D	P	R	V	E	L	D	D	U	R	S	N
S	O	S	U	U	P	T	O	L	D	R	T	I
D	U	B	S	J	Y	R	G	B	N	Y	U	P
K	Y	R	S	S	O	U	R	I	P	U	I	S
S	R	O	T	P	A	R	I	C	O	L	E	V
P	L	A	T	E	O	S	A	U	R	U	S	T

341. Color the picture following these instructions:

    a. Color the sky blue.

    b. Color the tree trunk brown.

    c. Color the leaves green.

    d. Color the farthest dinosaur gray.

    e. Color the nearest dinosaur red and green.

Answer: 339, Water, 8, 2, Tyrannosaurus rex.

342. Connect the Dots

Connect the dots from 1 to 38 to complete the picture.

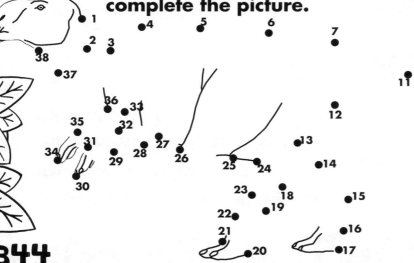

343. Color It!

Color in the picture.

344. Different Shapes and Sizes

Look at each of these dinosaurs.
Draw a line from each one to the word that describes it.

BIG

BIRD-LIKE

LONG

LITTLE

345. Draw Your Own

Draw a really thin dinosaur and a really fat dinosaur on a piece of paper.

87

346. Going For a Walk

Can you draw a scene around this dinosaur?

347. Describe the Scene You Have Drawn

348. Dinosaur Quiz

1. Name a plant-eating dinosaur with three horns on its head.

2. What animal is bigger than any dinosaur?

349. Draw

Draw the animal that is bigger than any dinosaur on a piece of paper.

88

Answer: 348. Triceratops, blue whale.

350. Friends Forever

This dinosaur can't find his way back home.
Can you find the path that leads to his friend?

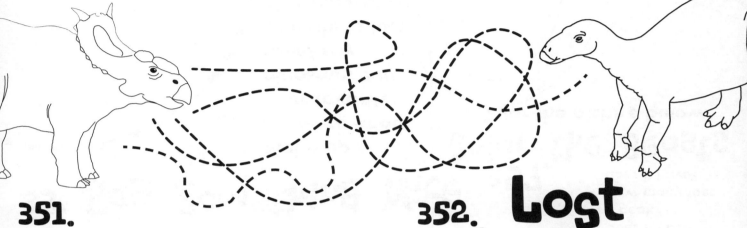

351. Dinosaur Map

Rearrange the letters in the last word to discover where the dinosaur bones are buried.

THE DINOSAUR BONES ARE BURIED IN THE WMSAP.

352. Lost Letters

This dinosaur name has lost some of its letters. Can you guess what they are?

TR_CER_TOP_

353. Make Your Own Map

Draw your own dinosaur map. Give places dinosaur names.

354. Dinosaur Facts

Choose the correct words from the lists to complete these sentences.

Stegosaurus was a   dinosaur, dog, plant

Tyrannosaurus was   fierce, friendly, cute

Brachiosaurus was   long, smelly, little

Stegoceras had a thick   brother, skull, book

355. Remember, Remember

Look carefully at the picture. Then cover it up and answer these questions.

1. How many spikes does it have?
2. What is its tail like?
3. Does it have a beak?
4. How many toes does it have?

356. Say Something Nice

Make up a sentence about your favorite dinosaur. You could say something like, "Tyrannosaurus was big and brave." Then draw a picture of it here.

90

357. Color the Beasts

Color the picture below.

Answer: 354. Dinosaur, fierce, long, skull.

358. Dotty Dinos

Connect the dots to see what the dinosaur is eating.

359. Storytelling

Make up a story called "Heterodontosaurus and the Sunny Day."

360. Finding Words

How many words beginning with the letter H can you find in the word HETERODONTOSAURUS?

361. Move Like a Dinosaur

Many plant-eating dinosaurs were very big and walked on four thick legs. They had a long neck and a long, whiplike tail. How do you think such a big creature would move? Get down on your hands and knees and move around like a dinosaur.

91

362. Missing Word

Draw over the dotted lines to see what the word is.

ROAR

363. Busy Dilly

Dilly has been busy. See if you can complete the words.

e_ _ _ _

n_ _ _ _ _

364. Copying Words

Copy the dotty word on the line below. Then color the Tyrannosaurus rex.

365. Color It

Color the picture, following these instructions:

Color Dilly green.
Color the eggs yellow.
Color the nest brown.

Answer: 363. eggs, nest.

366. What's Missing?

How many things are missing from the second picture?

367. Finish the Picture

Draw in the things that are missing from the second picture

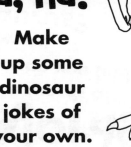

Ha, ha!

368. Just Joking

Can you match each joke with its punchline?

Q. What made the dinosaur's car stop?

Q. How do you ask a dinosaur if it would like a cup of tea?

Q. What do you get when a dinosaur blows its nose?

369. Ha, Ha!

Make up some dinosaur jokes of your own.

A. A flat Tire-annosaurus.

A. Out of the way.

A. Tea-rex?

93

370. Lovely Eggs

Can you decorate these dino eggs with different patterns?

371. New Words

How many new words of 2 letters or more can you find in the word **Nodosaurus?**

372. Make!

Make your own dinosaur. Draw your own dinosaur by mixing up the body parts of different dinosaurs.

373. All Mixed Up

The bodies of these prehistoric beasts are all mixed up. Draw lines to match the pieces.

374. What's So Scary?

Connect the dots to see this scary prehistoric beast.

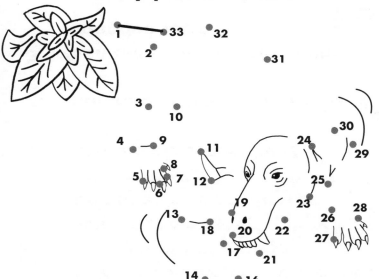

375. Hidden Picture

Color all the sections with dots to see a hidden picture.

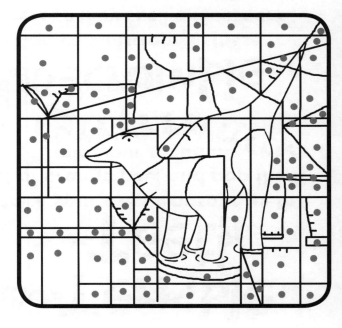

376. Scary Things

Draw a picture of some of the things on a piece of paper you think might scare a dinosaur. They can be as silly as you want.

377. Eat Your Greens!

Lots of dinosaurs enjoyed eating their greens. Draw some of the green vegetables that you eat.

378. Dinosaur Quiz

Read the words, then answer the questions.

> Dinosaurs lived millions of years ago. They were giant reptiles. In 1822 Gideon Mantell found the teeth of Iguanodon. Some people thought they belonged to a rhinoceros.

1. When did dinosaurs live?

2. What kind of animal were they?

3. When did Gideon Mantell find Iguanodon teeth?

4. What did some people think the teeth belonged to?

379. Color It!

Color the picture.

380. Terrible Teeth

Make your own dinosaur teeth out of orange peel and pop them into your mouth...

Grrrrrrrrrrr!

381. Unscramble

Can you unscramble these letters so they spell a dinosaur's different body parts?

ALIT

GLES   **ACLSW**

TEHTE   **PHI**

Answer: 381. Tail, legs, teeth, claws, hip.

96

382. Body Parts

Can you complete this crossword? The words are all parts of a dinosaur's body.

ACROSS
1. Long thing at the end of its body.
2. They used this to listen.
3. They kept their brain here.
6. They walked on these.

DOWN
1. They used these to eat with.
4. They saw through these.
5. They tore things apart with these.

383. New Words

Ceratosaurus was a meat-eating dinosaur. How many words beginning with the letter C can you make out of the word CERATOSAURUS?

384. Doing Words

Choose a doing word (e.g. going, walking) to complete these sentences.

The Pteranodon was _____ in the sky.
The Maiasaurus was _____ in the grass.

385. Coloring Fun

Color the picture.

Answer: 382. 1 across, tail; 1 down: teeth, 2. ear, 3. head, 4. eyes, 5. claws, 6. legs.

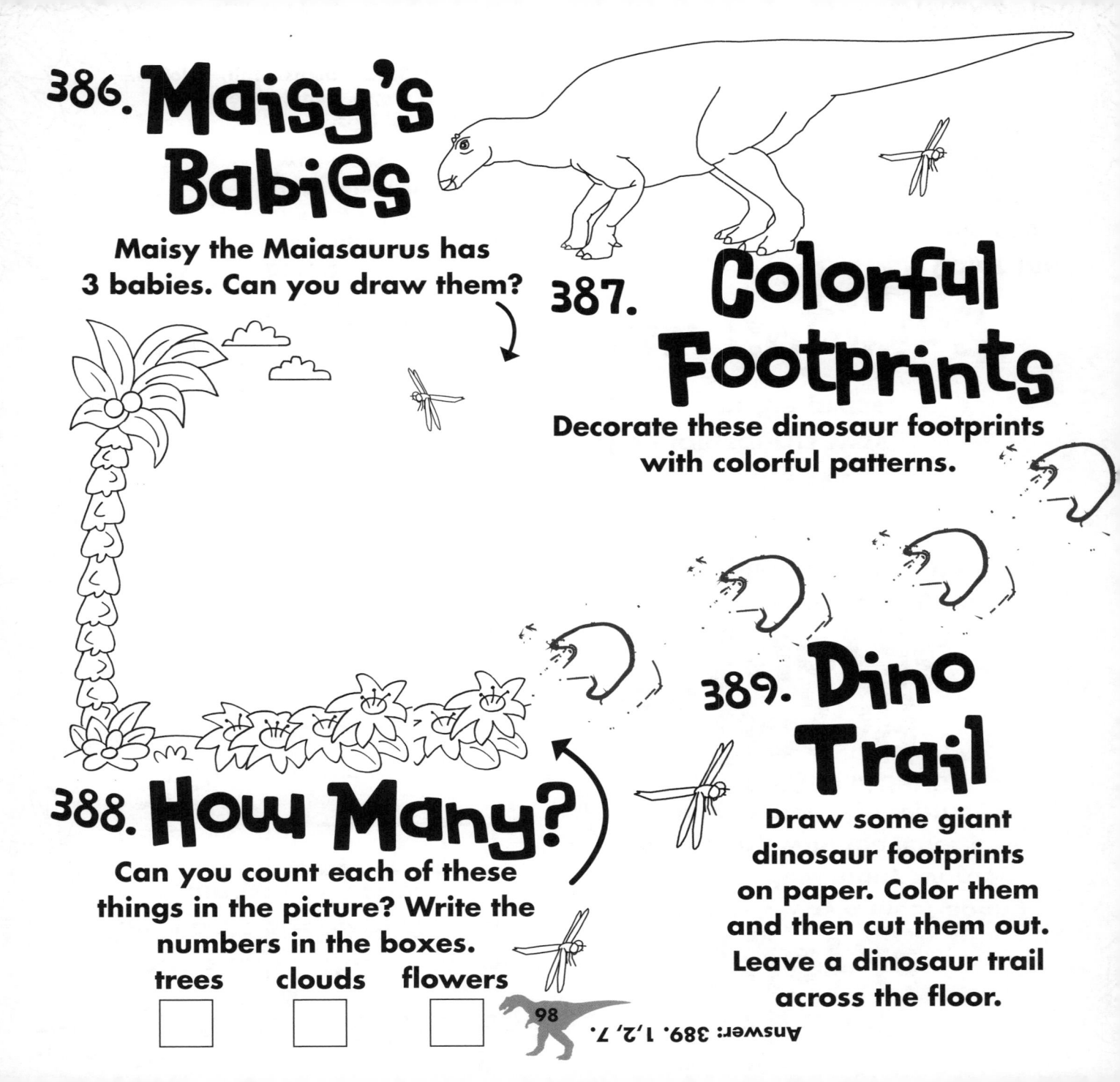

386. Maisy's Babies

Maisy the Maiasaurus has 3 babies. Can you draw them?

387. Colorful Footprints

Decorate these dinosaur footprints with colorful patterns.

389. Dino Trail

Draw some giant dinosaur footprints on paper. Color them and then cut them out. Leave a dinosaur trail across the floor.

388. How Many?

Can you count each of these things in the picture? Write the numbers in the boxes.

trees   clouds   flowers

Answer: 389. 1, 2, 7.

390. Different Dinos

Look at the dinosaurs. Draw an X next to the one that is different.

391. Copycat

Fill in the details in this dinosaur outline.

392. Color Them

Color all the dinosaurs that are the same one color. Color the different dinosaur a different color.

393. Which Dinosaur Is This?

Which dinosaur is this?

Stegoceras?

Sauropoda?

Tyrannosaurus rex?

Answer: 393. Sauropoda.

394. Dinosaur Number Race

Throw a dice, then color a space above the dinosaur with the same number on it as you have thrown. Keep on throwing until one of the dinosaur numbers reaches the finish. Which dinosaur won?

Finish

Start

1   2   3   4   5   6

100

395. Dinosaur Quiz

Look carefully at this picture. Then answer the questions.

How many clouds are there?
What are in the background?
What is the weather like?
What does the dinosaur have on his back?

396. Coloring Fun

Color in the pictures in on this page.

397. Dinosaur Land

Make your own prehistoric landscape in a shallow cardboard tray. Stick on an egg cartoon to make it hilly. Dab on some glue and sprinkle on some sand. Stick on twigs, leaves, and bits of dry grass. Glue on some aluminum foil to make a pool.

398. Long Dinosaur

Unscramble the letters to spell out the name of a long dinosaur.

I L S
O P C D
O U D

399. Funny Dinosaurs

Take one sheet of paper and draw a dinosaur head at the top. Fold it over and pass it to your friend so they can't see what you have drawn. Get them to draw a dinosaur body. They will fold it over and pass it back. Draw the bottom half of a dinosaur. Unfold the paper and have a good laugh.

Answer: 398. Diplodocus.

400.
New Dinosaur

Make up a new dinosaur. Draw it here and write its name.

401. Who Am I?

Can you guess who I am?

1. I am a gentle plant-eater.
2. I am very long.
3. I used to be called Brontosaurus.
4. I have a small head and a tiny brain.
5. My name begins with A and ends in S.

403. Extra Bits

Which bit belongs to the dinosaur above?

402. Let's Pretend

Pretend that you are a dinosaur expert looking for fossils. Where would you look? What would you do with the fossils when you found them?

Answer: 401. Apatosaurus.

404. Dinosaur Tail

Draw the tail of the Utahraptor.

406. Painting Fun

Splash some paint on a sheet of paper. Fold it in half and press hard. Unfold the paper and leave it to dry. Once it is dry, see if you can turn your splotch into a dinosaur.

405. Dinosaur Vowels

This dinosaur name has lost all its vowels. Can you put them back in to reveal what it is?

the vowels → A E I O U

BR_CH_ _ S _ _R_S

407. Dinosaur Knowledge

Decide whether these sentences are true or false. Put a check ✓ in the yes or no box.

	yes	no
a. Stegosaurus had bony plates on its back.		
b. Tyrannosaurs only ate plants.		
c. Diplodocus had long, sharp teeth.		
d. Coelophysis could fly.		
e. Brachiosaurus means "arm lizard."		
f. Protoceratops had a voice like a parrot.		

Answer: 405. Brachiosaurus.
407. a yes, b no, c no, d no, e yes, f no.

103

408. Back to Front

Put the letters below in the correct order to spell out the annoying dinosaur's name.

ROTATIRRI

410. Word Chain

How many dinosaur names can you find in this word chain?

409. Dinosaur A-Z

Believe it or not, there is a dinosaur named for each letter of the alphabet. How many can you think of?

cardiplodocusrarebrachiosaurusderapaytgauryslodentrosaurusrrtspohosaurshs

411. Dinosaur Places

Read each word backward to see where each dinosaur came from.

A. Oviraptor
B. Kentrosaurus
C. Baryonyx
D. Albertosaurus

1. Ailognom
2. Acirfa
3. Dnalgne
4. Setats Detinu

413. Missing Letters

This dinosaur name has lost some of its letters. Can you put them back in?

K E _ _ R _ SA _ R _ S

412. Word Grid

Can you find these words in the grid below?

dinosaur   rock   leaves   teeth
cave   nest   baby

D I N O S A U R
B S E V A E L O
A T N A E V A C
B Y C O O M N K
Y U N E S T P B
T E E T H D Y A
U A S O N I D W

414. Armored Dino

Connect the dots to see who this dinosaur is.

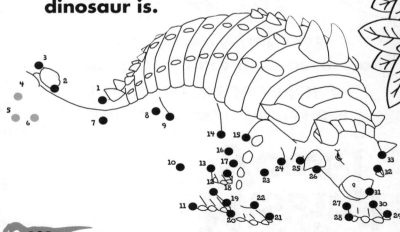

105

415.

Who Am I?

Do you know what this dinosaur is called? Here are some clues.

My name means "well-armored head."

I had a bony club at the end of my tail.

I had spines down my back.

416. Lunchtime

Make up a story about this Tyrannosaurus rex and his lunch!

417.

Color One

Color in the T-rex picture as brightly as you can!

418.

Missing Vowel

These dinosaur names are all missing the same letter—sometimes more than once. Do you know what it is?

St_goc_ras
Tric_ratops
Sup_rsaurus
_dmontosaurus

419.

T-rex Dinner

Now draw some things that you think the T-rex might like to eat.

Answer: 415. Euoplocephalus. 419. e.

420. Identical Dinos

Which two dinosaur pictures are identical?

422. Shortcut

Minmi wants to get home to bed. Find the shortest route home by solving the math.

Route A: 5 miles – 2 miles = ☐

Route B: 10 miles – 8 miles = ☐

423. Making Sense

Can you make this sentence make sense by putting the spaces between the words in their proper places?

Di nosa ursliv ed al ong tim eago.

421. Twin Set

Color the two identical dinosaurs the same.

424. Letter Jumble

Can you find a dinosaur name hidden in this pile of letters?

A
l b U
e o r u
t r s a s

107

425. Spare Parts

This dinosaur is missing his tail. Draw him a tail to complete the picture.

427. Messy Letters

Rearrange these letters to find the name of a large meat-eater with an S-shaped neck.

losaurluas

426. Food Steps

Help this dinosaur reach his breakfast by spelling out his name starting at the arrow.

428. Missing

Fill in the missing letters of these words. Look at the pictures for clues.

ST_G_S_UR_S

BRE_KF_S_

H_NGRY

429. Spiky Fun

How many spikes does this dinosaur have? Why do you think he has them?

431. Corythosaurus

How many new words beginning with C can you make from the word **Corythosaurus?**

430. How Many?

How many prehistoric creatures can you count below?

432. Funny Colors

Make the picture even sillier by coloring it in using the brightest colors you can find. Maybe some of the dinosaurs could be pink and purple.

433. Match Them Up!

Which two of these pictures are exactly the same?

434. Color Them Both

Color the two matching dinosaurs.

435. True or False

Which of these sentences are true and which are false? Tick the ones that are true.

1. Tyrannosaurus rex was a vegetarian.

2. Euoplocephalus had spines.

3. Spinosaurus liked to spin wool.

436. Missing Vowel

These dinosaur names are all missing the same letter – sometimes more than once. Do you know what letter it is?

H_AYANGOSA_R_S
O_RANOSA_R_S
IG_ANODON

437. Copy and Color

Copy this picture into the grid.
Then color it.

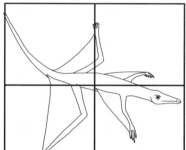

438. Name Game

Fill in the missing letters to spell out the dinosaur's name.

St_ra_osa_r_s

439. Word Puzzle

Write the first letter of each word to spell out the name of a dinosaur.

Star, egg, igloo, seal, mouse, onion, sandwich, apple, umbrella, rocket, unicorn, sun

440. Patterned Dinosaur

Draw a dinosaur on some Styrofoam. Get an adult to help you cut it out. Dab paint on the Styrofoam dinosaur. Then press it onto paper to create a dinosaur skin pattern.

Answer: 438. Styracosaurus, 439. Seismosaurus.

441. Dinosaur Word Grid

```
S W T I T A N O S A U R U S
U A M Y J T G H F S Q A U K
R U V U I H M L M U C L F O
U L R W N F H A A P Q B R S
A N F I L Y E V K E V E R A
S P J D O Q P W N R S R B R
O X K U G J D J Q S T T C E
M Z J V B Q A Y C A W O S C
S Y A B Y H Z S W U N S W O
I O U W K Q T U A R U A V G
E L A P A T O S A U R U S E
S B D R T M Z T I S R R L T
X P Q O K K S T O J R U D S
Y M R O T P A R I V O S S N
```

Find these words in the word grid above.

Albertosaurus   Oviraptor
Apatosaurus   Stegoceras
Seismosaurus   Riojasaurus
Titanosaurus   Supersaurus

442. Letter A

How many dinosaurs can you think of beginning with the letter A?

443. Shadow

Which shadow belongs to this prehistoric reptile?

444. Guess My Name

I am a huge dinosaur whose name means "earth-shaking lizard." My name has 12 letters. It begins with S and ends with S.

112

445. Dino Park Rules

Some of the words on this sign have been replaced with pictures. Look at the pictures and write the word in the space below.

please do not:

eat the

_____

stomp on the

_____

lay [eggs] in the grass

_____

have a nice day!

446. Making Rules

What rules would you make if you had dinosaurs living with you? Write them down and put them up on your bedroom wall.

447. Pet Dino

What kind of dinosaur would you like to have living with you? Draw a picture of it!

448. Color

Color in some of the prehistoric beasts that live in the Dino Park

449. Backward Dinosaurs

These dinosaurs' names have all been written backward. Reverse the letters to find out what they should say.

NODOORT

_ _ _ _ _ _ _

ROTPARIVO

_ _ _ _ _ _ _ _ _

SURUASOTAPA

_ _ _ _ _ _ _ _ _ _

450. More Dinos

Write some other dinosaur names backward for your friends to figure out.

451. Describe it

Describe this dinosaur's face. How is it different from your face?

452. Decorate the dino!

Decorate the dinosaur's face.

453. Drawing Time

Can you draw designs on Allosaurus's body, starting at his nose and finishing at his tail?

454. Talk to Me

Make this dinosaur say something funny by filling in the speech bubble.

455. In Reverse

Read this word backward to find out the dinosaur's name:

SURUASOTNODORETEH

456. Quick Question

Tyrannosaurus rex lived in:
A. The ocean
B. North America
C. London

Answer: 456. B.

457. Look and Remember

Look carefully at this picture. Then cover it up and answer the questions.

1. How many dinosaurs are in the picture?
2. What other creature is there?
3. How many leaves are on the tree?
4. What is in the sky?

458. Coloring Fun

Color the picture.

459. Break the Code

Can you break the code to see what this sign says?

2=a, 4=b, 6=c, 8=d, 10=e, 12=f,
14=g, 16=h, 18=i, 20=j, 22=k, 24=l, 26=m,
28=n, 30=o, 32=p, 34=q, 36=r, 38=s, 40=t,
42=u, 44=v, 46=w, 48=x, 50=y, 52=z

28 30   8 18 28 30 38 2 42 36
38 46 18 26 26 18 28 14

-- --------- ---------

460. Secret Letter

Use the same code to write a note to a friend. Make sure you let them have the code so they can work it out.

461. Mixed Squares

Write the numbers 1-4 underneath these squares to show the correct order of the pictures.

  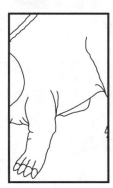 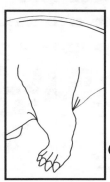

____   ____   ____   ____

462. Writing Fun

Copy the dinosaur's name PROTOCERATOPS here.

463. Missing Parts

Can you see 5 things missing from the second dinosaur?

464. Making the Same

Draw on all the missing parts to make both dinosaurs the same.

465. Finish the Picture

Finish drawing this picture and then color it.

466. Broken Names

Can you match up the letters to make dinosaur names?

STEGO   MI
TRICERA   TOPS
EUOPLO   CERAS
COMPSOG   NATHUS
MIN   CEPHALUS

467. Explorer

How many of these objects can you find around the page?

bone ☐
rock ☐
leaf ☐
cloud ☐
egg   ☐

468. First Letter

Say each of these words. Can you think of a dinosaur that begins with each of the beginning sounds?

tree, car, sock, arrow, elephant, house

118

Answer: 466. Stegoceras, Triceratops, Euoplocephalus, Compsognathus, Mimi

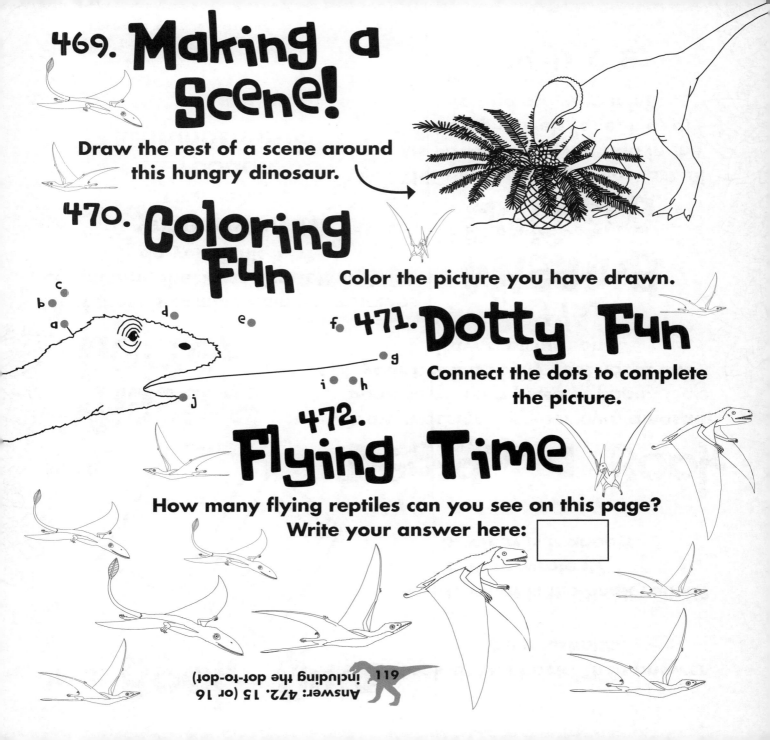

469. Making a Scene!

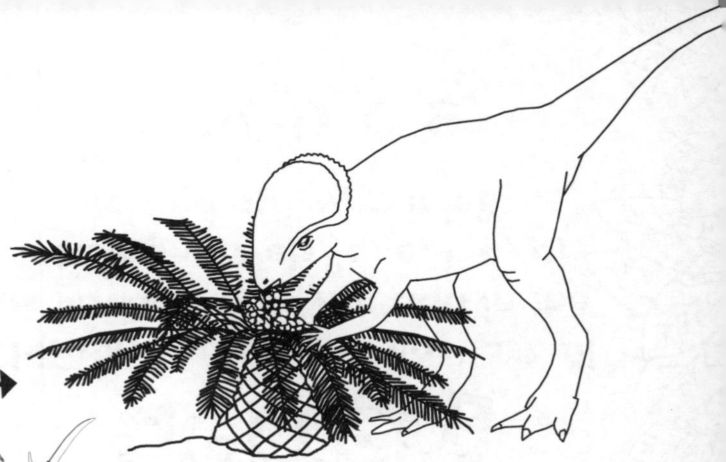

Draw the rest of a scene around this hungry dinosaur.

470. Coloring Fun

Color the picture you have drawn.

471. Dotty Fun

Connect the dots to complete the picture.

472. Flying Time

How many flying reptiles can you see on this page?

Write your answer here: ☐

Answer: 472. 15 (or 16 including the dot-to-dot)

473. Book Quiz

Look at this book. Then answer the questions.

Prehistoric World
by Hope E. Saurus

A dictionary of dinosaurs and other creatures

1. What is the book called?
2. Who wrote it?
3. What is it about?

474. Missing Letter

All of these scrambled dinosaur names are missing the same first letter. What do you think it is?

___yrannosaurus
___riceratops
___roodon
___itanosaurus

475. Design a Book

Draw a design for your own dinosaur book cover on a piece of paper. Give your book a really cool name and draw a picture on it.

476. Missing Letters

This dinosaur name has lost all its vowels. Can you add in the missing vowels (a, e, i, o, u) to find out who it is?

D_PL_D_C_S

477. Funny Fern

Trace around the leaf from start to finish without taking your pencil off the page.

start and finish here

478. Scrambled Word

Rearrange these letters to spell out the name of a small, fast dinosaur.

OODNOTR

479. Yum, Yum

What is this dinosaur thinking about? Rearrange the letters to find out.

L E S E V A

480. Draw it In.

Draw what the dinosaur is thinking about. Then color the picture.

121

481. Missing Sail

This dinosaur is missing the sail from its back. Can you draw it in?

482. Read and Answer

Read these sentences and answer the questions.

> Sauropods, the largest dinosaurs, ate plants. They had long necks that helped them reach up into trees. They had thick legs to carry their huge bodies.

1. Who were the largest dinosaurs?
2. Did they have short necks?
3. Why did they have thick legs?

483. First Letters

Write the first letter of each word to discover the name of the dinosaur.

pig, leg, apple, tent, egg, owl, saw, arm, umbrella, rabbit, unicorn, sausage

_ _ _ _ _ _ _ _ _ _ _ _

122

484. Pairs

Can you find the two that are exactly the same?

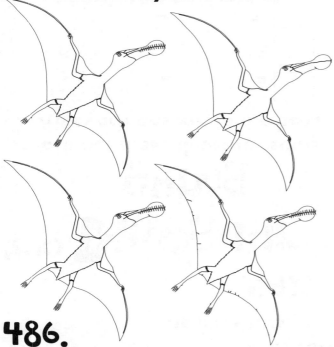

485. Wings!

Design some wings for this flying reptile to catch his dinner with.

487. Mixed-up Halves

Draw lines to match the two halves of each prehistoric beast.

486. Dinosaur Spelling

Write the letters of the alphabet 4 times on paper and cut out each letter. Mix up the letters and give them out equally to yourself and a friend. Then see how many dinosaur names each of you can spell.

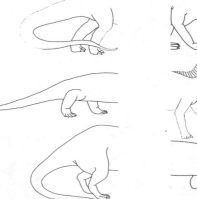

488. Finding Words

How many new words can you find in the word Liopleurodon?

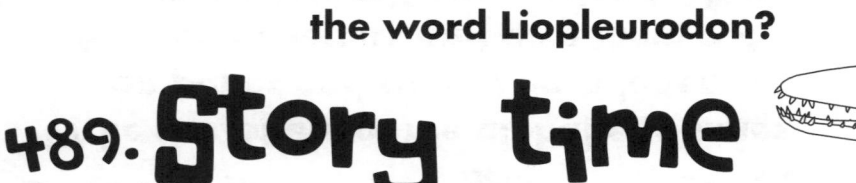

489. Story time

Make up a quick story about sea-living reptiles such as pliosaurs.

491. Coloring fun

Color the reptile and add some fish for it to eat!

490. Dinosaur sums

Work out these dinosaur sums. Write each answer in the box.

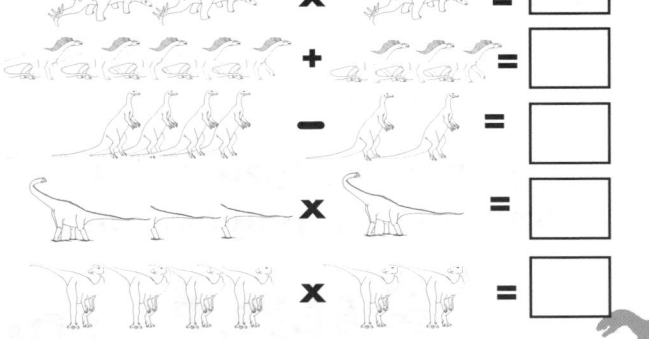

492. Drawing Time

Follow the instructions to complete this picture.

1. Draw spots on Camptosaurus.
2. Draw the sun in the sky.
3. Draw a tree.
4. Draw footprints on the ground.
5. Draw some rocks.

493. Yes or No

Answer yes or no to these questions.

1. Could any dinosaurs fly?
2. Did T-rex and Triceratops live at the same time?
3. Were most dinosaurs meat eaters?
4. Did some dinosaurs eat other dinosaurs?

yes	no

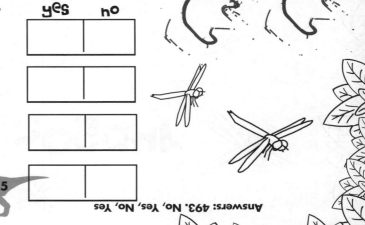

125

Answers: 493. No, Yes, No, Yes

494. Scrambled Dinosaur

How many new words can you find in the word Megalosaurus?

495. Make a Beast

Trace this prehistoric beast onto paper. Cut it up into pieces and mix them up. Try to fit them back together again.

496. Who Is It?

Do you know who this dinosaur is? Here are some clues:

1. It was a relative of T-rex.
2. It lived in North America.
3. Its name means "lizard from Alberta."

Answer: 496. Albertosaurus

497. Dinosaur Day!

Think of what a dinosaur might have done during a typical day (hunt, eat, sleep etc.), then act it all out with your friends.

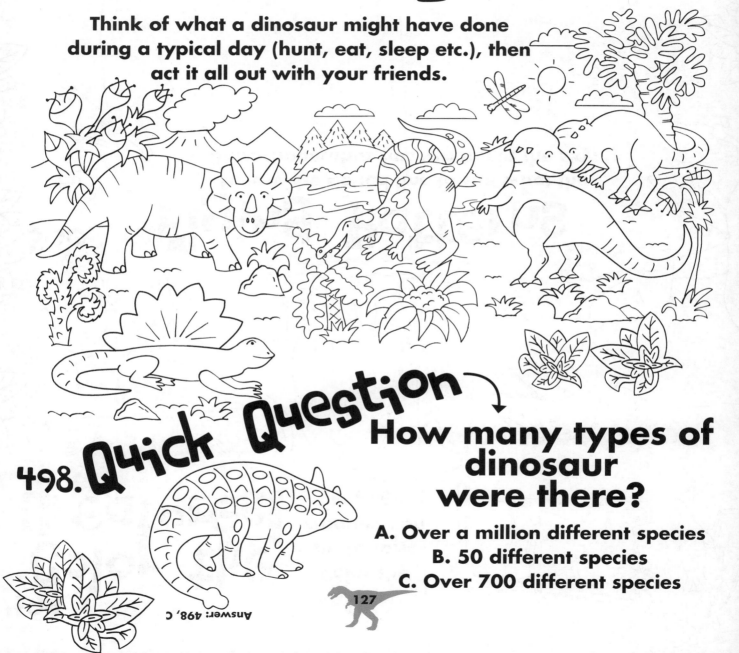

498. Quick Question

How many types of dinosaur were there?

A. Over a million different species
B. 50 different species
C. Over 700 different species

Answer: 498, C

499. Color the Creatures!

Color the prehistoric creatures on the page!

500. Flying Patterns

Follow the dotted line to see what the Batrachognathus has written in the sky.

Goodbye!